Praise for "Intent"

Justin's understanding and practical application to sport with technology is revolutionizing the game. His ability to make my decisions easier and more informed have continually proven to be accurate and correlated directly to performance. The knowledge in this book is something that any strength coach, performance professional, or trainer would find very informative.

— Dallas Eakins
Former NHL Coach, Head Coach San Diego Gulls (AHL)

A combination of practicality and science, the program in this book brings an element of understanding in the everyday work and development of our athletes.

— Enrico Blasi
Head Hockey Coach Miami University RedHawks

Devan has rapidly established himself as one of the bright young coaches in the hockey world. Not by writing on the internet but by helping to develop a winning program and by turning college players into NHL players. His common-sense approach and integration of sport science into a well-developed strength and conditioning program has been a key, and this book outlines that approach.

— Mike Boyle

Devan's practical approach to sport science and the system he has built during our time together has made a significant impact on the long-term development of our players. This book will be a valuable addition to your library for hockey coaches and strength and conditioning coaches alike.

— Norm Bazin
Head Hockey Coach UMass Lowell

This book presents key sport science processes that support athlete development and success at any level. Given how integral science is to sport, the value of this book is that it highlights just how to use systematic scientific processes to both evaluate and protect athletic talent development.

— Dr. John P. Sullivan
Sport Scientist/Clinical Sport Psychologist/Consultant
Author of "The Brain Always Wins"

D1594853

INTENT

A Practical Approach to Applied Sport Science for Athletic Development

INTENT

A Practical Approach to Applied Sport Science for Athletic Development

Justin Roethlingshoefer
and Devan McConnell

ISBN-10: 1-946702-09-9

ISBN-13: 978-1-946702-09-8

Freeze Time Media

Cover illustration by Di Freeze

Contact Justin:

Instagram: @innerstrength19 and @thehockeysummit

Twitter: @jroethstrong

Contact Devan:

Twitter: @DMcConnell29

Instagram: @DMcConnell29

To my parents, thank you for giving me the opportunity to do what I love. To my sister, thank you for supporting me. To all my coaches and mentors, thank you for helping pave my path through this industry.

Justin

To my coaches and mentors over the years, thank you for your direction. To my parents, thank you for your support. To my wife, Erica, thank you for all of your love. And to my kids, Finnegan and Dublin, thank you for your inspiration.

Devan

Acknowledgments

We would like to thank the following people for their help in this process:

Mark Fitzgerald for his Foreword

Dallas Eakins for his Foreword

All the players who have helped Devan and me come up with this system

All the coaches who have allowed us to implement it and make us better

JJ McKeever, our main editor

My mom, Evelyn, for her editorial assistance

Di Freeze, for tying it all together

Contents

Foreword (Sport Coach)

There are many factors that go into having success in a game or a season. Are you setting your team up for success before the game even starts? Sleep, nutrition, and fitness will have a direct effect on our minds and our readiness to excel. Are you going off "feel and opinion" when it comes to fueling, workload, and recovery, or are you tracking and setting a plan for those three components? Because in the end they will have a huge impact in how you start, execute, and finish a game.

In this book, you will find some of the most advanced and practical applications of human performance analytics and how to set up a program that will enable your team to succeed. The time, thought, science, and most importantly, human element included here will allow you to begin implementing things in your team the very next day no matter your budget.

As a professional hockey coach, I have come to understand how these things make a difference in performance night in and night out, but I also see the difference it makes in player development and player health no matter the age. The system in this book works. I have seen it firsthand, and am glad to have had a part in it.

Every day strive to be better, every day strive to make others better, every day have Intent.

Dallas Eakins,
San Diego Gulls Hockey Team Head Coach
Anaheim Ducks Top Affiliate

Foreword (Strength Coach)

In the world of high performance, utilization and implementation of sport-specific monitoring is crucial in building long-term athletic success. With a recent explosion in sport technology, coaches must educate themselves further in order to wade through a growing list of products and gadgets aimed at performance personnel.

Construction of a high-performance model starts with an in-depth understanding of both the athlete and sport, as well as the ability to remove the clutter of data collection in order to find the important pieces, which will ultimately paint the picture of performance.

Two of the best young strength and conditioning coaches in the field, Devan and Justin, have put together a playbook that allows any coach to begin to institute this high performance model, helping to reach a deeper level of athlete readiness.

These are two individuals who spend the majority of their time in the trenches coaching, which makes this book so much more valuable. They are those coaches who work with athletes at every level and deal with the 'real life' issues surrounding athletes like travel, game play, injuries, sickness, and of course on an emotional and personal level.

"Intent" was written to provide a light in the fog of sport science and data collection, to give the performance coach at any level a tool to decipher metrics collected through each and every device available. As a strength coach at any level and with any type of budget, having a better understanding of where your athlete needs to improve, both on and off the field of play, is crucial to understanding athletic performance.

This book will serve as architecture of an efficient high performance program and provide valuable insight well past any piece of technology.

Mark Fitzgerald,
Anaheim Ducks Head of Performance
Under Armour Global Training Team
Elite Training Systems Owner

Introduction

As with most things in sports, the role of the strength coach has evolved over the years. Besides structuring a weightlifting regime for athletes and coaching proper form when lifting, now we conduct a variety of drills and testing to help players become faster, quicker, and stronger. We are constantly finding new methodologies to fine-tune our athletes. No matter what sports you are involved in, you know that being a little stronger or faster will pay off when a game or race comes down to millimeters or fractions of a second.

While both of us have been involved with other sports, currently we are both working with hockey at the college and pro levels. We utilize different aspects of sport science to give our players an edge and to assist head coaches in planning their practice and game strategies. We want to share what we do and what we have learned from others. Everybody who works with sports wants winning as part of their DNA. While the work we do helps provide head coaches with a physically and emotionally better-prepared athlete, we believe the testing and training also assists the players in preventing injuries, sickness, or to recover from an injury.

We recognize that our readers may be from all different areas of sport. Our goal is to provide information in a way that is accessible to strength coaches, sports coaches, players, and anyone else who has an interest in guiding athletes to realize their full potential. We hope we strike the right balance of providing theoretical and practical information that you can easily translate and apply to your sport.

There are a few concepts we want to present in this introduction about the work we do and the content of this book.

Our work as strength coaches enables us to:

- Allow individual programming while maintaining team mentality.

- Identify individual positional needs.

- Create trust and buy-in with coaches and players

- Provide accountability between coaches and players

- Allow programming for different levels of the sport (college vs. pro)

The role of a strength coach or someone fulfilling that role for a team is to help the player become a better athlete. A strength coach's job is not to show a player a better way to pass the puck, pitch a baseball, or defend against a pass. We are there to take the raw material of an athlete and work with him to become better prepared to display those characteristics through power, strength, speed, and ability to repeat those efforts consistently.

For example, we will talk about jump tests in the book as a way to test for power. If doing a test, we see that a player's right leg is stronger than the left, then we work on a program to get the power equal between the two legs.

We might have athletes hooked up with heart rate monitors so that we can measure their exertion. This gives us valuable data on where their conditioning level lies and where we need to focus that individual's cardiovascular training. This helps determine how long a player should be out on the ice during a game before returning to the bench to rest.

First of all, everything presented in this book is applicable to all sports. Many of our examples are from hockey, as that is our life right now, but we believe the applications are transferable to any athlete in any sport. We are not talking about techniques specifically geared to hockey, but for all athletic endeavors.

While we will talk about those two brief examples in more detail in different chapters of the book, please notice that we do use the words "measure" and "test." You will see that a great deal throughout the book. Like any science, "sport science" accurately means constant testing and successful compilation of data. The more facts you have, the more you can assist your players.

You want the training you do with your players to be quantifiable. You might shy away at first to translate so many physical activities down to a number, but it is the best way to communicate what you are doing with your players and coaches. Plus, if you work for a team with a large roster, it is the easiest way to keep up with all the players that might be in your charge.

Contrary to what you might think, recording this information does not turn your players into a "number." Rather, it creates their own individuality. You both know what they can do, and the type of work needed to increase the scores on the different tests you perform. This type of training improves certain characteristics to ensure further development of the athlete. It is about breaking down the team from a group into individuals. When you help each player, and they reassemble as a team at practice and game time, the cumulative effect of improved athletes will be that much greater.

Part of that individuality is that you can customize training by position. In hockey, we have three types of players: forwards, defensemen, and goalies. They all have different physiological and mental approaches to the game. Football has even more unique positions where the players need specialized attention on their development. While you can use the various methods here on every member of the team, what you want to extrapolate from the data you gather and then apply to the player is going to be different according to the player's role on the team.

Measuring athletes and giving their tests different numerical values helps when you share your information with the coaches. When you can share that Player A is more fatigued this week and back it up with data, then the coach will be able to set up practice in a way that will allow for a more prepared athlete come game time.

We always guard against undertraining or overtraining players. Sometimes it is a razor's edge between the two. When you have data to refer to, you can accurately track how a player is progressing and adjust workouts and practices accordingly. The techniques and concepts we talk about in this book allow you to prepare your athletes properly. We have a lot more control doing that during practices than in games. Working with the coach, you can pace practices for what a player and team can do.

As for the structure of the book, we are going to talk about a variety of techniques, equipment, and technologies for testing, monitoring, and measuring athletes. As we will point out more than once, we know all sports programs are different in what they can do regarding budget and personnel. We are not offering a set, comprehensive plan to implement, but rather, many different options from which you can choose. Even if you can only do the simplest form of any of the techniques here, then you are already benefiting your players.

At the end of each chapter, you will find a "gold, silver, bronze" list of equipment you can consider for your program. This list is by no means exhaustive. We constantly attend seminars and research new techniques, equipment, and software coming on the market. Do not be afraid to Google any of the topics we talk about and explore what else is out there. You can do wonders with some simple, inexpensive equipment or even with pen and paper.

While we talk about what works for us, there are other methods of tracking and testing you can use. Research and determine what will best suit the needs of your program. That is true with all that we discuss in this book. There are often many ways to accomplish the same goals. The bottom line is the same: keeping the players healthy, developing them as athletes and people, and preparing the team for an opportunity to win.

1

Sport Science

Today's athletes have more information available to them than ever before on nutrition, training techniques, and the monitoring of strength, fitness, flexibility, and just about any other metric available. In this technologically advanced age, sports face the same problem as any business or institution that compiles extensive data. What do you do with it and how is it useful?

That is what we want to answer for you in this book. While both of us have extensive experience working with hockey players in the college, minor league, and NHL level, the lessons we have learned in working with our athletes apply to all sports. Our goal is the same as any athlete, strength coach, or sports coach — to have our players operating at peak effectiveness in competition when they need to be their best.

As performance coaches, we are directing most of our information that we have accumulated through experience toward our peers in all sports at all levels. However, we are presenting it in such a way that it is also easy for athletes and sports coaches to understand what we are describing. We want to make it easy to apply the concepts and ideas we present. As stated above, everyone has the same desire: for the athlete playing the game to be at his optimum level of fitness and to perform as well as possible in his sport. When you have healthy athletes at the top of their game, many good things can occur.

We have kept that idea in mind throughout the writing of this book. We have taken great pains to keep the concepts and language understandable to all, and to build each chapter in a logical sequence so that no reader gets lost in the descriptions. We know that when we talk to athletes and coaches sometimes, we start to throw around all the jargon and acronyms that we use on a day-to-day basis. It can be overwhelming if we do not take the time to explain things. We want to use language everyone can understand. In that way, others can take these dynamic concepts and make it work for them.

As you read through the chapters, you will see that we are giving you an outline of a practical approach to applying sport science to your sport as we apply it to ice hockey. Again, our methods and techniques are perfectly adaptable across all sports. You will see how easily applicable our approach is because it is not a set program. Our intent here is not to give you an established boilerplate program that you can copy and simply use. We certainly do not use the "copy and paste" approach to what we do with our teams. Rather, we want to give you a holistic model so that you can provide your athletes with a better-integrated sports performance system.

The reason we believe that this is the best approach is for several reasons. Those reasons all come under the banner of "One Size Doesn't Fit All." Let's explain.

First, we are very conscious of the fact that not all programs in any sport are the same. You might be managing a program at the high school level where every dollar is a struggle to find. You might be the assistant coach of the team who doubles as the strength coach, or you could very well be the head coach, and you wear all the hats — even bus driver when needed! In these days, there are high school programs that can be on par with a college team in a certain sport, but that is the exception. The reality is that you might have to battle with every sports team in the school for a time in the weight room or to use the court, field, or ice. In this day of belt-tightening in high schools, many athletic programs are learning to make do with less.

The same is true in the college ranks. Quite often, the resources in Division I are greater than at a Division III school. That does not mean the Division III hockey or football team does not want to make use of the best techniques to get better. When resources are at a premium, working smarter or being aware of the cutting edge in fitness or the intricacies of a certain sport can make all the difference. While we might have opinions on the best way to execute a power play in hockey, that will not be the topic of discussion. Our role and expertise is the physical development of the athletes, not tactical game strategy. We are going to ground ourselves in helping you use the cutting edge in training your athletes that we have utilized and developed to help our players.

We also know there is a difference if you are involved with minor league hockey, baseball, or some sport at the lower end of the professional spectrum. If you have a team of athletes not quite ready for the big time yet, then you may not have the resources of the Los Angeles Dodgers or Philadelphia Flyers. That does not mean you cannot incorporate any of the techniques and technology we will discuss. We know from experience that budgeting will be a factor in what you can do and we hope we can present options that any program can utilize. The little-known reality is that even at the top of the athletic pyramid, funds are often hard to come by in the strength and conditioning and sport science landscape.

Whether you have all the money in the world or have to worry about how much athletic tape you can afford, we believe you will find ideas in this book that you can utilize. The size of your program and the staff you have available are important considerations as you go through the chapters. Keep that in mind as you find ideas you like in this book. It is certainly okay to prioritize what works for you in your particular situation. Logistics always matter, and what looks good on paper might not look good in practice if the resources and environment do not fit.

Besides the size of the budget and organization, no two athletes are alike either. Probably the key to all that we have learned is that you cannot train any two athletes the same way. One of the foundations of almost everything we will share with you is that each concept helps you tailor a training program for an individual. If your team's nickname is the "Wolves" or the "Wolfpack," you are probably aware of the saying, "The strength of the wolf is the pack, and the strength of the pack is the wolf." In other words, how good each player is will determine how good the team is while the team's strength will help the individual be that much better.

In our role as strength coaches, we strive to help each member of the team to stay healthy, strong, and fast so they can be the best athlete possible. However, we could not successfully do our job if we did not have the cooperation of the athletes, coaches, and the rest of the staff. There is no doubt that it takes buy-in from everyone involved to move forward with the different concepts we will explain. However, once the team experiences the positive results, the desire will increase among everybody to participate in as many aspects of what we share in this book as possible.

Finally, we are very conscious that all coaches are different. None of the ideas in this book can occur without the head coach's consent. You have some coaches who pounce on every new technical advance that might give their players an edge. You have some who cannot seem to get enough data to help them make player decisions and game plans. Then you have some old school coaches who believe that running or skating endlessly in an attempt to build "mental toughness" is the best way to prepare for their sport. If you aren't the head coach of the team, then you have to present these ideas that you want to implement to that person. We will discuss scenarios and tactics for "speaking coach" later in the book. If you are the head coach, we hope to convince you that our ideas will help your athletes reach a new level, and, in turn, do the same for your team.

All sports teams are different, so this book does not lay out a set program. We would be doing you a disservice even trying to do that. As it is, we work with teams on opposite sides of the country with athletes at different levels, and we *know* what works for one of us will not exactly work for the other. There are similarities, of course, with what we do with our teams. However, we customize our approach to fit the specific team we are working with at the time.

Maybe the best way to think of this book is as an à la carte menu. You do not have to order a specific meal at the restaurant as they list it. Instead, you can choose your salad, appetizer, soup, main course, veggies, etc., that you want. Think of this book exactly like that and you can decide what menu items are best for your situation.

Our other consideration with not giving you an established program is that we use a very holistic approach to training our athletes. This means you have to look at everything involved with individuals in helping them perform better. You cannot help athletes without looking at their nutrition intake. If you want them to become faster, then have you set up the correct strength and power development program for them? You want to keep them strong, but at what point do you adjust what they do to optimize both strength and speed? When you take the holistic approach, it is more work for both you and the athlete, but the results are going to be so much better.

Strategy is a component of all sports. You need to think through every situation and have options for any scenario. Developing an athlete is the same. You need to consider what you want to do with an athlete four or five moves down the road. You have to factor in practice time, nutrition, sleep, strength and conditioning work, etc., into what they are doing so that they can realize their full potential. However, that is not all. You also need to appreciate the mental factors of a game: preparation, studying the next opponent, getting prepared for each practice, travel, and the stress of the games themselves. If that is not enough, most players have to worry about school, relationships, family, etc. If they are competing at the professional level, they have the additional commitments such as media requirements, money, and keeping their job. When you work with an athlete, you have to know what that person is going through in order to customize their training plan so that they will get the most out of it.

We kept all of this in mind as we constructed each chapter. For the most part, each chapter will concentrate on one theme like "Training Load" or "Jump/Power Profiling." Our goal is to give you enough tools in your toolbox so that you can pull out the ones you need that fit your team. Remember...and we cannot emphasize this enough...you do not have to do everything at once. If you do, you will be overwhelmed, and probably break your budget. It is perfectly fine to start out with a hammer before you advance your way up to a nail gun. That is true with all the technology we are going to introduce you to throughout the book. In many ways, this is how we began with the utilization of sport science, and this book is the collection of experiences we have had on that journey.

We want to encourage you to develop a system from the material we have written about here. The nice thing that we have discovered is that once you start establishing a methodology that works for your athletes and coaches, it becomes easier to add to it. Depending on where you are in your program right now, some of this might be brand new for your people to begin using. There is going to be a breaking-in period for all involved. Once you get over the initial hump, though, you will find athletes and coaches looking for more new training techniques to implement. If you already use some of this, then we hope you get new ideas about other technology you can incorporate into your system or better ways to use what you already have.

A word here on technology that we want you to keep in mind. It is a tool. Granted, most of it is much more advanced than a blade sharpener, pitching machine, or blocking sled, but you need to know how to use new technology as well as you do the old standbys. A shiny new monitoring device is just taking up space if you do not take the time to know how to use it, and to best figure out how it fits with your program. Do not get distracted by something bright and shiny you see at a trade show or online. If you do not see a use for it in the near future, put it on your wish list for later. If you do purchase equipment, learn everything you can as quickly as possible about it. A good rule of thumb is to make sure you run the technology and not let the technology run you. Have a plan for how you are going to implement the tool, as well as how you are going to utilize the data.

We will discuss case studies in each chapter to show how the technology we discuss has practical applications. Implementing any science is not perfect, and sport science is no exception. Like us, you are going to have trials and errors. We think one of the benefits we offer with our book is that we already made some mistakes that you can skip!

Regarding how to implement the technology, we also want you to know how to organize and use the data you gather. That will be a big part of each chapter. All of this will be worthless if you do not know how to apply what the technology tells you. In business, there is something known as "data paralysis." This is where the information pile is so large that it is almost impossible to sort through it and find what is useful. It is another good reason not to worry about doing everything at once. When you start slowly and consistently, you can learn both the technology and the benefits of the data. As you add to it, each piece becomes a building block for the next one. You will not be overwhelmed, and everything you do will seem like the logical next step. Think of it as going from a fifth grader in a sport in the town recreation league to the professional ranks. For 99.5 percent of athletes, it is going to be necessary to go to high school and then to college or a minor league before hitting the big time!

The objective of the work we perform with athletes, coaches, and teams is to have everything we do in training lead to developing a better player. For us, we want to help our hockey players to be the best they can be on the ice. We do not have players do anything that is work for work's sake. We also want to reduce the incidence of injuries as much as we can.

This philosophy carries over to how we look at sport science. We want to have better answers to whatever questions arise in the preparation and development of our players. In fact, we like it when what we do leads to even more questions about how we can assist our players to improve. When that happens, we have to find the answers. When we can dig deeper into the problem and the data surrounding it, we are finding other ways of influencing the physical development of our athletes, which in turn, leads to more success as a team.

Our holistic approach to performance coaching is to use quantifiable data that directly correlates to on-ice success. You want to use the same criteria for any training you do in your particular sport. If it is not helping your players, it has no place in your program. This seems obvious, but as the saying goes, "common sense isn't too common." In training, you want any tracking and monitoring you do to help inform your coaches on player readiness come game day. The utilization of sport science in the team setting really comes down to trying to improve the level and consistency of an individual's performance and be able to transition seamlessly from training and practice to the game itself.

Finally, we will remind you again and again that no technology or data stream is ever going to replace coaching or having a relationship with players. Sports is all about people. Sports are popular on many levels, but remember that it is the ultimate reality show. Nobody knows what is going to happen when the first pitch is thrown, or the puck is dropped at center ice. You have people who are being stressed physically and emotionally to extreme levels by the pressures of the sport. And that is just the coaches! The players have to deal with all of that every day as they train and practice to achieve to the best of their ability.

Never get so hung up with the technology that you forget about the athlete. Some kids love sports but have a low-stress tolerance. They get overwhelmed easily, and that might be in little league or junior hockey! If you are a performance coach or have that responsibility to a team or an individual athlete, you have to listen to your players and know the people you are working with. Communication is key, and data should back up and inform, not dictate decision-making.

When you know you were instrumental in helping your players and coaches achieve excellence, you will have an incredible feeling of achievement and satisfaction. Let us help you reach that point.

One of our players doing some on-ice sprint work.

2

Internal Load Metrics

You always hear about athletes having heart. This is their desire to play as hard as possible utilizing their skills to the best of their ability. When an athlete has "heart," you know he is going to give 100 percent effort. This concept often extends to the performance of an entire team. A team with "heart" is going to give their all in a way that makes the players and fans understand that they are not going to give up regardless of the challenging circumstances they face.

Having that desire and dedication to a sport and teammates cannot be dismissed as something that does not matter in athletics. It very much does and is often that quality that a coach looks for as one of those intangibles that separate a good athlete from a great one. However, when performance coaches talk about the heart of the athlete, we mean the organ that pumps blood through the body. This muscle pushes oxygen and nutrients via that blood through the circulatory system. Whether you are an athlete or not, keeping your heart operating at peak efficiency is paramount to your health and well-being.

In the case of an athlete, that heart and cardiovascular system need to be operating at greater efficiency than non-athletes. This is true whether you are talking about the high school, college, or pro level. A participant in sports requires his body to do more than a sedentary person or someone who is only fairly active. With an athlete, so much comes down to how well the cardiovascular and energy delivery systems are functioning. This includes when a player is at rest, at practice, during a game, and when in recovery mode after that practice or game.

What is nice about technology today is that we are past the days of only having a stethoscope to monitor the heart. It is also not necessary to be reclining in a chair hooked up to an electrocardiogram — also called an EKG or ECG — to find out how the heart and cardiovascular system are functioning. Now we can fit an athlete with monitors that allow us to see how her cardiovascular system is performing in real time. This gives a coach, strength coach, and the player raw data to develop the best practice plan for the athlete. Granted, heart rate monitoring is only one component you need to look at when evaluating a player's physiology, but it is an important one.

This wearable technology is big in the athletic world today. When deciding how you want to monitor your players, make sure that the data you are collecting is something that you can use to benefit the athletes and the team. To illustrate this point, we want to share with you the practical applications of monitoring heart rate and various metrics of workload and exertion. Here are three key reasons why we believe measuring internal training load via heart rate monitoring technology is important in a team sport setting:

1. To gain better insight

2. To ask better questions

3. To attack the 1%

We talked a little about gaining insight into your players by monitoring their heart rate. Accumulating as much information on an athlete as you can helps you have a better understanding of what is going on physiologically inside the player. The better information you have, the more opportunity you have to help him improve and succeed, instead of just guessing at what the problem and solutions are. As a very simple example, when a player says to you, "My legs feel heavy" or "I don't feel very quick today" you have physiological information that might help you pinpoint the reason.

One thing we have learned while engaging in internal monitoring of our athletes is that as soon as our process gives us an answer to one question we might have on a player, it seems to open another slew of questions immediately. For instance, you start out looking at the overall fitness and health of the team. To do this, you break down the data to the individual level, looking at the specific performance of each individual. As you work with each athlete, you are gathering your heart rate and work-load information. This is what we mean by asking better questions. The data from internal training load monitoring will begin to paint a picture. As that landscape comes into focus and you begin to understand the specific areas, you will begin to see that there is often more than meets the eye.

You will discover as you accumulate info that you will try to break it down into as much usable information as you can. You then find yourself going full circle. You set up an optimum program for a player, and then you move on and do one for each member of the team. After that, you are trying to figure out how to optimize workouts for the entire team so that it helps each member. You keep seesawing between working with players individually and the team as a whole.

The more you discover from working this process, the more you want to know. You will see an improvement in an athlete's performance and, by extension, the team. Nothing motivates as much as success, and your results are going to encourage you to refine what you do so it is even more beneficial to the players and the team. Do not be afraid to further your research and ask questions of your colleagues to bring your monitoring program to a higher level.

All athletes are different. Some athletes are going to leap in ability due to good training, practice, and coaching. However, at some point, all athletes reach a level where any increase in their athletic capacity is going to start to peak. From here, any additional progress will be incremental. This is where attacking the one percent comes in.

Heart rate monitoring and other measures that we talk about in this book come into play to help athletes maximize their marginal gains.

When an athlete reaches a certain fitness and performance plateau, you are looking for those small improvements that will continue to make the player perform better. The idea of the "aggregation of marginal gains" is that small, seemingly insignificant daily decisions have the ability to add up and compound over time. Making small improvements to an athlete or a team on a day-to-day basis leads to large improvements in physical development, capacity, and output over the long term.

A performance coach wants to know the stress placed on a player's metabolic, cardiovascular, and nervous systems during his workouts, practices, and games. Too much consistent stress is going to lead to chronic fatigue. Chronic overload is when athletes burn out, see a decrease in performance, and an increase in central nervous system (CNS) fatigue. This can lead to injury, insomnia, and inconsistent performance. In fact, one of our concerns that we want to monitor is how we taper down our players' workouts from an internal metric standpoint. We make sure we factor in weekly and yearly tapering to avoid chronic fatigue and overloading our players. Creating acute overload in training is necessary for growth and development from a cardiovascular standpoint. This is done through yearly planning that breaks each day down by "loading" metrics. It is just as important to make sure a player has a sufficient rest and recovery time.

A very simple example illustrates this concept. A player's heart rate might show that if he has a practice the day before a game that is very intense, his heart is not beating as it should during a game. The onset of fatigue from that previous day's practice is going to affect his ability to exhibit high threshold efforts consistently during game time. The ability to recover between bouts might be diminished, making the recovery times longer, and the capability to withstand high power efforts is diminished as well. You can then consult with the coach and show with the pertinent numbers that if the player has a less intense practice the day before a game, he is more likely to be at peak performance for the game physiologically. In reality, the volume of the high-intensity practice day may have a minor negative effect on the player but could be the difference between a win and a loss.

Now let's add some complexity to the example to show how you can structure an optimum workout and practice schedule for a player.

In many sports, the different positions athletes play are going to have diverse effects on their internal metrics. The goaltenders, forwards, and defensive players in hockey put their bodies through various stresses and changes during a game. For example, a goaltender:

- Plays 60 minutes

- Position is more aerobic than others

- Requires bursts of repetitive explosive movements

- Pre/post game lactate differential is least of all the positions

- Typical highest body fat percentage

- Lowest anaerobic capacity

- Lowest anaerobic power

- Lowest VO2max

- Very technical position

Contrast that with forwards:

- Top two lines play 20-22 minutes

- Average shift length of 43 seconds

- Anywhere from 17-27 shifts per game

- Cover more distance than any other position

- Higher anaerobic demands than defensemen

- Typically higher VO2max and anaerobic power/power output

- Highest acceleration numbers/shift

Then there is the defense:

- Top defensive pairings play upwards of 30 minutes

- Average shift length of 47 seconds

- Anywhere from 23–32 shifts per game

- Intensity duration is less

- Higher work-to-rest ratio

- Anaerobic power/power output is less than forwards but greater than goalies

- Fewer high power accelerations than forwards

At full strength, there are six hockey players on the ice at one time. As you can see, you have three different sets of players who have to approach a game in their own way. It is not that the stress of flying down the ice is better or worse than a goalie concentrating on the intricacies of his position; it is just different. When you track how a player's heart rate and other vital signs are functioning in a game or practice, you have your data from which you can make decisions on the structure of that player's training plan and practices, as well as utilization during a game.

Most sports are going to have athletes working their bodies differently. The stress a wide receiver goes through is different than an offensive lineman. A quarterback has the mental load of running a team to contend with as much as what he does athletically. A 100-meter swimmer has to approach training differently than her teammate that swims a 1000-meter race. Your sprinters and shot putters are going to have different body types and training regimes. The point is that you need to take the time to address the workload of the different positions contained in your sport. When you break that down, you are in a better position to aid the players in those roles. You do this by creating a needs analysis of each positional player. You can break it down into physical, conditioning, speed/power, strength, and mobility. Monitoring and measuring internal training load allows you to develop a more in-depth understanding of the physiological demands of each position within each sport, and that, in turn, will drive what you do from a preparatory and developmental perspective.

You can see more considerations go into fatigue that you need to factor in about our player from the original example above. This is why we collect data and quantify it with a number. However you assign values to the internal metrics you collect, those numbers will be consistent for your team. Then you can easily see how each player is doing according to your data. With that information, you can explain what is going on, to the player or coaching staff, and demonstrate why the intensity of practices should be a certain way. We will go into talking to players and coaches later in the book, but the important point is that you have solid information to make decisions to help the player become objectively better.

In sports, the little things matter in being successful. By this, we mean the fundamentals: blocking, tackling, skating, stick handling, throwing, catching, running the bases, shooting free throws, etc. A good coach works the players almost to craziness by stressing fundamentals. Performing them perfectly can make the difference in the game. Monitoring your players to give them the same edge in maximizing the physiology of their bodies is just as important. In all phases of the game, it is the little things that make the difference. Attack your one percent!

Technically, heart rate monitoring encompasses the collection and analyzation of various metrics. The most common metric that everyone understands is beats per minute (BPM). Our body works harder; the heart works harder. It has to beat faster so we have enough oxygen-enriched blood feeding all parts of the body so that the person can continue what he is doing. As a person becomes acclimated to pushing the body to a certain level, the heart rate will take longer to speed up when doing something physical. This is called efficiency, and it is the level of fitness we want our athletes to attain.

By monitoring heart rate response to training, we can determine the intensity of the work being performed by a player. This, in turn, allows us to prescribe appropriate training workloads to create significant, but not undue, stress on energy systems. Appropriate stress allows the cardiopulmonary system to adapt favorably, thereby improving "fitness."

There is a saying normally applied to the study of history that goes, "You don't know where you're going if you don't know where you've been." The same is true of monitoring the heart rate of an athlete. You need to know that player's heart rate when he first comes into the locker room for the season. Be sure to continue the process all through his first workout and practice. This is the information you will build on. It becomes your baseline as you chart the player's progress or setbacks.

This is science you are dealing with here. A big part of science is to carefully and consistently record all measurements and observations. As a coach or strength coach, doing those things is necessary to make this program work for you. From the first day you begin working with a player, you have the responsibility to chart all data on that athlete you deem important. As you ask good questions, you might find yourself adding to the list of items you want to record. Remember, it is all a process and not a procedure set in stone. As you gain new insight on what you can learn from monitoring heart rates of players, the more you can refine your program.

One of those insights we learned from heart rate monitoring is TRIMP or "training load" depending on the system being used. As you know, there are different ways of determining the effect of exercise on an athlete. One of these measurements is called "Training Impulse" or TRIMP (TRaining IMPulse). The simplest way to explain it, as it does have a slightly complicated formula, is that it provides a real-time as well as post-training data point that is easily interpretable as "work load." The harder a player works (increased HR), or the longer he works, or a combination of both, will increase the TRIMP score.

See Appendix Images on Page 136

In a session where two athletes are performing the same work, the athlete with the higher score can be said to have worked harder to perform the same task. TRIMP creates an easy way to evaluate the overall amount of physiological work done. This info can be used to inform the coaching staff about the need to back off or go harder in the future. It can also be used to gauge whether or not recovery work is necessary, and to evaluate the relative fitness of an individual or the team as a whole.

Interestingly, when sports coaches first come into contact with heart rate and internal training load information, they often want to know "how hard" someone worked. The player with the lower TRIMP or similar workload score is commonly thought to be the athlete who is giving it his all. That might be true, but what we really want is the athlete who gets the job done with the lowest workload score. This is a sign of efficiency. It is similar to the idea of gas mileage in a car. With all things being equal, you are going to want the car that has better gas mileage. The one that has to work harder and is less efficient ends up burning more fuel and probably breaking down sooner rather than later.

TRIMP/min or "Intensity Density" is a more nuanced way to look at TRIMP data. Since TRIMP is a function of both heart rate response and duration, two variables affect it. TRIMP/min breaks this info down further to showcase the relative workload. For example, two practices might have the same overall TRIMP score of 90. However, practice A lasted 90 minutes, resulting in a T/min of 1.0. Practice B ran 45 minutes, resulting in a T/min of 2.0. Even though the total load was the same for each practice, B was much more intense. This is crucial to understand the relative intensity of a session, and not just the overall load, will have implications for physiological improvement, fatigue, and readiness.

What this allows you to do is tailor workouts and practices to both an individual and the team. Your monitoring data helps a coach schedule all aspects of training with the goal of having the players being able to perform at peak efficiency when it matters most — during the game. One complaint you do not want to hear from the players is that they left their best efforts on the practice field or ice or court. Like everything we are discussing in this book, heart rate monitoring is another tool in the coach's arsenal to prepare the team for competition properly and effectively.

Another caveat you can pull out of heart rate monitoring is heart rate variability (HRV). This is a measurement of time between successive beats of the heart. The time frame, and whether it is stable or variable, is an indicator of the relative balance between the parasympathetic and sympathetic branches of the autonomic nervous system. The utilization of an HRV measurement allows for a physiological assessment of the recovery state, or balance, between fatigue and readiness.

The sympathetic branch of the autonomic nervous system is often referred to as the "fight or flight" system. The parasympathetic is known as the "rest or digest" system. Depending on where an athlete falls on the continuum from one to the other, you can determine a great deal about his ability to adapt to stress. From a performance standpoint, it helps decide if you should utilize training/high-stress loads, or recovery-based training on a day-to-day basis. HRV provides an objective measurement of "readiness." This is a more concrete indication of an athlete's performance rather than just asking how he feels.

Depending on what equipment you use for heart monitoring, you will be able to keep track of your players' heart rates in all aspects of their day. You can do this when the player is away from practice, during workouts, and, except at the pro level, in games themselves!

We mention monitoring a player away from actual sports-related activities because how his heart acts during the day is as important as when he is working out or playing. For instance, the resting heart rate (RHR) indicates how a heart is beating when a person wakes up. Research shows that the RHR is a strong gauge of a person's fitness level and is a vital indicator of overall cardiovascular health. If you discover one of your players has a high RHR when they wake up, they might be on the verge of some negative cardiovascular event. It could also be an indication that you need to adjust something in the workout schedule for that athlete. Whatever the case, monitoring a player's heart as much as possible is going to allow a coach to help keep that person healthy. In the grand scheme of things, that is always our number one priority.

When we advocate our ideas to coaches, we might run into one or two main pushbacks to our methods. The first are old school coaches who are skeptical of what to do with all this data. They did not grow up or participate in the technical revolution as it happened. Much of their coaching relies on experience and instinct, which, if they have been coaching for a long time, is pretty darn good. Their idea of practice and getting players ready for a game is doing what they have done forever. In our sport, this might be "the commitment skate" to get the team to a better fitness level.

What we have discovered by working with various teams and coaches is that marrying the two together makes the players and team better. Nothing beats experience and feel for a game. Coaches who mix in data and metrics find that they can take a team to a new level. Just as you try to find that one percent where you can help a player be a little bit better, utilizing data like heart rate monitoring can help a team find that slight edge they need to beat their biggest rival.

Another hesitation coaches might have is that all of this sounds great and something they would like to pursue, but it sounds too sophisticated or expensive for their program. They worry about the time needed to track and analyze data — if they can obtain the necessary equipment.

First of all, heart rate monitors for athletics have been commercially available for at least ten years now. A good thing about technology is that it tends to become cheaper over time and this equipment is no exception. By all means, we encourage teams to research and look for equipment that best fits your budget and manpower situation. We know that depending on the type of team you coach, you might only have a handful of people doing everything with the players.

Even the simplest monitors give you basic information that will help you better understand the "internal training load" of a player's various sessions and the intensity level of the workouts. You can start out by recording "AVG Heart Rate x Session Length" to give you a rough estimate of training load. This will let you compare training sessions, practices, and games, so you can determine the optimal way to train. For example: if you record an average HR of 150 beats per minute during a 45-min training session, you can quantify this training load as $150 \times 45 = 6750$. You can use this number to compare against other training sessions as a general marker of your overall exertion.

For teams that have the luxury of a sizable budget and staff, we want to assist you with refining your training program with these proven concepts. We all want to improve our program and to maximize the energy system development of our players. As we talked about, you can take heart rate monitoring and constantly analyze how to use and refine the data to benefit your team. As with the equipment, continue to research how to maximize the use of your players' information.

One thing that is true of both knowledge of the human body and technology is that it is always changing. The cutting-edge equipment of today might be passé by next month. Studies are going on in all fields of physiology to explore how our bodies work. A certain belief in how you are conditioning a player might be circumvented by a new study. Of course, next year's study might then refute the new study and you discover how you were doing things was the best. In other words, keep up with the research for both tech and human fitness. In our field of work, the only constant is change!

See Appendix Images on Page 137 through 140

Gold - Silver - Bronze

Gold - HR Team System

Heart Rate Team Systems, such as those by Polar and Firstbeat, track individual heart rate metrics within the team setting, such as HR, %HR-max, calorie expenditure, TRIMP, and other workload metrics. All of this data can be utilized in both real time as well as post training to maximize physical development and better understand total workloads and stress applied to the athlete.

- Firstbeat

- Polar

- Zephyr Anywhere

Silver - Individual wristwatch/ personal HR belt

HR metrics are readily available on an individual level by using HR belts that sync to wrist watches. This is a common tool in the running and cycling world, as athletes have long known the benefit of basic heart rate information to guide their own training. These tools can be used on an individual or small group setting with team sport athletes as well.

- Polar

- Suunto

Bronze - Pulse oximeter, hand counted pulse

Pulse oximeters are inexpensive tools which measure pulse rate through the tip of one's finger. Similar to what a nurse might apply to a patient at a hospital, these provide quick and accurate data any time an athlete can be monitored. The tried and true method of hand counting pulse provides a cost-free alternative to measuring heart rate, and along with some basic pen and paper tracking, can provide valuable insights into fitness and recovery.

- Medical Test Supply

3

External Load Metrics

P eanut butter and jelly. Pancakes and syrup. Salt and pepper. Knife and fork. Macaroni and cheese. Some things go together naturally. In sports, the optimum combination for an athlete is speed and strength. Whatever the game, an athlete who can develop these two qualities is going to perform better.

Each sport is going to have different goals for a player depending on the requirements of the game, as well as the positions within it. A hockey player needs a different level of speed and strength than a tennis player. A sprinter's training is going to be different than the guy who throws a shot put. You might think that speed in a sport like golf is almost a nonfactor, but a player is going to hit the ball longer and better if there is a nice balance between a golfer's strength and the speed he swings the club. In some sports, like American football, players on the same team are going to train differently depending on their position. A wide receiver requires a different balance between speed and strength for running and catching the ball than an offensive lineman needs to push people out of the way.

The point is that the regime for strength and speed is going to vary by the athlete. What is consistent is that measuring what that athlete is doing is important. As the science of the human body advances, we have enhanced ways of conditioning the body and determining results. Increasing an athlete's time in the 40-yard dash or how much he is bench pressing are still great indicators of progress. However, there are tools and methods available that help us "read between the lines" of how a person performs. It is the ability to analyze how a person runs, jumps, or lifts weights that allows strength and sports coaches to tweak a player's training program to help the athlete realize his potential.

As we are talking about the technology to help you increase the strength and speed of your players, a measuring term you will come across in your research is 1RM. For the uninitiated, this stands for "one-repetition maximum" and is the standard gauge of measuring the strength of an individual. Simply stated, it is the maximum weight a person can lift for one repetition while using the proper technique. This common measurement allows a coach or trainer to determine strength capabilities and imbalances, as well as assess the status of the athlete's training program.

As a standard of measurement for an athlete, you can use 1RM for various exercises such as split squats, back squats, bench press, and just about any other discipline found in the weight room. It helps provide a baseline for each of your players and gives you a measurement in which to track their progress.

An important area of our work with our hockey players is Velocity Based Training (VBT). We are first going to look at VBT as it applies in the weight room. One of the best experts on this subject is Bryan Mann. In an article from elitefts, Bryan says:

"Some days the weights feel light; some days they feel heavy…This is essential because our nervous system is never constant. In their review paper from the Australian Strength and Conditioning Association, Jovanovic and colleagues used formulas by Jidovtseff to estimate a daily 1RM through the load-velocity profile. They noted an approximately 18% difference above and below the previously tested 1RM, meaning that there was a 36% range around the previously tested 1RM.

"For example, if you had 80% of the 1RM listed for that day, the actual relative load may be 98%, which would be way too heavy for that day, or it could be as light as 62%. This is why some days we feel

strong in the weight room and some days we don't. The absolute load is not the same relative intensity that we had preselected. We wanted the 80% based on the previously tested 1RM, but today that prescribed 80% is actually 98% of the individual's capability for that day, so it's way too heavy."

He goes on to describe why this is important: *"By understanding the corresponding velocity, or even more simply the trait that is to be developed, the proper load can be selected load for that given day. It does not matter what the % of the 1RM is supposed to be for that day because by utilizing a prescribed velocity, the individual will automatically be at the appropriate load. Now, as we had previously mentioned, the velocities fit in line well with the original Bosco Strength Continuum. From lightest to heaviest, the continuum is as follows: 0-15 is neurological and untrainable, 15-40% is starting strength, 40-60% is non-quantifiable, 65-75% is accelerative strength, and 80-100% is absolute strength."*

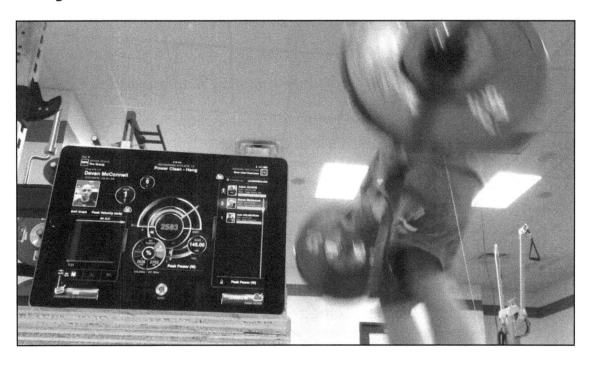

The use of VBT devices in the weight room allow for quantification and specific prescription of power-related training variables.

An accelerometer is a device used to measure the velocity in which a player lifts a bar or dumbbell, or any other similar equipment. This allows us to measure several different aspects of strength that a player should develop. For us, it helps to see exactly where we need to change an athlete's training regime to increase a deficient area. For the athletes, they immediately see if they are getting closer to their goals. That immediate gratification is a great motivator for players. Technology has helped with making training more interesting for the athletes since you can tap into their competitive nature to quickly show them if they are performing adequately in an exercise.

While VBT allows for different metrics, we want to condense them into four categories:

1. Max Strength – The ability to move a high load at a very low velocity. In essence, you want to move a lot of weight without any limit on time.

2. Strength Speed – Moving a high load at medium velocity.

3. Speed Strength – Moving a moderate weight at a high velocity.

4. Starting or Explosive Strength – Moving a light load very quickly.

As you can see, the lighter the weight, the higher the velocity of the exercise. Conversely, if an athlete is lifting something heavy, the movement is slower. Once you determine the exercises you want an athlete to perform, or at least the key performance indicators for your program, you can record what his 1RM is for each and use that as the measure from which to chart improvement.

We cannot stress enough that one size does not fit all on the subject of VBT, or of much else in athletics. While the needs of players in hockey might be different than those in baseball, the needs for each athlete on one of those teams are also going to be different. As a coach or trainer, you need to conduct a needs analysis for each player so that they are going to get the most out of their workouts.

As performance coaches, we look at the situations our players encounter during a game. We want our players to develop high levels of acceleration and speed for moving up ice or changing direction. They need power for shooting at the goal and strength for gaining position along the boards. Hockey players have to be able to absorb force and have good mobility in all their joints. Since hockey players tend to be out on the ice for short amounts of time, their conditioning has to be conducive for them to perform in short bursts and quickly recover before they return to the ice.

How we map out the four VBT metrics for our players, and the relative amounts of each specific strength quality that is necessary for optimal performance is going to be different than a soccer coach or a golf coach. Once you know how to balance out the need for strength and speed in your sport, you can then set up a program tailored to each player. Let's take a closer look at the variety of activities you can put your players through with VBT.

On one end of the strength/velocity curve, you have heavy load exercises such as various squats and deadlifts. These exercises may be performed at high loads but relatively low velocities. This would be in the "Max Strength" area of VBT. On the other end of the continuum, you have very low-load but high-velocity exercise, such as plyometrics, sprinting, and various medicine ball throws. These exercises, and some more classical barbell movements such as the hang snatch, are relatively light but are very high velocity. This is the "Explosive Strength" end of the VBT guide. Between the two ends of the force/velocity curve are "Strength/Speed" and "Speed/Strength." These qualities are often developed via tools like dynamic effort squats and presses, and other Olympic lift variations such as hang cleans. The important consideration with choosing the exercise and speed is what specific quality you are trying to stress and create adaptation in.

Using Velocity Based Training allows the coach to figure out the proper type of training to use throughout the year. Depending on your sport, your goals during the offseason might be different than what you want your athletes to achieve when games are in full swing. As we briefly mentioned, VBT helps to keep your players interested throughout the entire year. It is difficult for any athlete to give 100 percent all the time. It is easier in competition, but the drudgery of training can seep into any good player's motivation. With VBT, you can give a player an immediate objective regarding how much faster they need to move a weight or to work toward a heavier load. You can turn this into a competition among the players and use that competitive spirit to encourage them.

For a coach or strength coach, VBT also gives you a great barometer of the readiness of an athlete on any given day. A player might do great lifting one day, but it hurts his ability for the next day or two. When you track this information, you can optimize the program for players so that they are at their peak for game day. As you are adjusting an athlete's program, you can employ different methods based on the athlete's performance and goals.

For example, a player could be overworked. It might be necessary for you to adjust to a lower amount of weight for each set in a session while encouraging the player to maintain the same velocity. Another adjustment might have the player lift the same weight for each set, but the set ends if he drops below the required velocity. Then on the next set, you see if the player can do more reps. By adjusting the load to ensure the exercise is performed at the appropriate speed, the athlete can respect the state of his nervous system and not over or under train. This is known as "autoregulation."

You can experiment with different adjustments for each player. The important thing is to record what happens in each set throughout the workout. All of the metrics in the world are useless unless you have a system to record and track them so that you have a consistent measure of each player. There are many systems available at different price points to give the athletes and coaches real-time feedback during training. Also, you are accumulating information that is objective and can help you analysis performance whether you are doing it for one workout, the season, a year, or even a career. As we constantly suggest, do your research to see what will work for your situation and budget.

Another type of tool which falls under VBT is a speed assessment/manipulation device. These tools, instead of measuring the speed of the barbell in the weight room, measure the speed or displacement of the athlete during sprints or jumps. Again, there are different products on the market, but what you want is a speed assessor and adjuster. One that we use comes in a box with a strong, but very thin cord wrapped around a carbon-fiber drum. A laptop connected to the box monitors and controls the resistance or towing strength of the cord through an electric motor. The computer also records the force and speed applied to the cord as the athlete runs, and you can see everything recorded on the screen.

This device measures the speed of an athlete's motion using various common tests. All data is instantly viewable and allows you to determine:

- Short Speed - Test acceleration from 0-50 m in any direction, minimal or heavy loads.

- Top Speed - Measure maximal velocity, including the acceleration phase.

- Repeat Speed - Assess sports stamina with distances up to 90 meters.

- Multi-Directional Speed - Compare movement patterns in any direction.

- Change of Direction Speed - Measure the ability to change speed in any motion.

We want to share with you a practical example of how to use the device. Our example is from hockey, but you can extrapolate the applications for your sport. Here we combined the testing for both dry land and on-ice workouts. This data was accumulated over a six-week period from a training camp and concentrated on sprint and jump testing of the players.

Every two weeks, we did on-ice testing with specific procedures for skaters and goalies. Skaters did more sprinting on ice using various leg and arm positions while goalies did more short maneuvers like butterfly slides that they use in game situations. The dry land testing was a daily practice. The tests included a standing long jump and single-leg lateral jumps. These exercises have a direct relationship to skating prowess.

The analysis gave a great deal of insight into player performance. Summing up the results, players who did better on the jumps achieved a better speed to peak power and rate of force development. Between the two jumps, the single-leg lateral jumps most closely mirrored the on-ice components. Guided by the results, the strength coaches and skating coaches coordinated their training for each player. The skating instructors translated the off-ice training into on-ice performance through drills, cutting, and additional mobility work.

By the end of the training camp, the coordination between data and practice methodology produced a notable increase in on-ice power production. Several players increased their peak and average power over a six-second sprint by 10 percent. Players reduced the asymmetries between legs, in some cases with the previously weaker leg producing more power on the end-of-training test than the dominant leg performed on the arrival test.

Besides the noticeable results, this technology allows us to do a fast and accurate assessment. By running the entire team through the long jump and single-leg lateral jump on both legs in about 20 minutes, it becomes an effective part of their training *and* testing. "Test" and "retest" are the terms you want to drill into your staff and players. The more testing you do, the more data you have in helping your players develop and improve. The more information you accumulate on any one test, the easier it will be to see patterns as you map out an athlete's progress.

We are sure when you apply similar methods and equipment to your sport, you will be able to develop progressive results for your athletes. Once you establish baselines for each player, you can easily track improvement. Like with monitoring the load-lifting aspect of VBT, these speed tests are a way of determining fatigue in a player, especially as a season wears on. When a coach can figure out when a player is getting worn out, then it is easy to modify the athlete's training to bring him back to peak efficiency.

Timing gates are another valuable type of technology to measure various aspects of an athlete's acceleration and speed. The most common use is for testing a player performing sprints though timing gates, but some variations of the equipment can also measure reaction time and vertical jump height. Measuring sprint times with this technology is much more accurate than using a stopwatch and provides a reliable measurement of speed.

See Appendix Images on Page 141 through 143

In general, timing gates make use of an infrared signal and detectors. When a runner breaks the beam, the gates digitally record the results. By using different formations, the gates can be used for a single sprint, repeat sprints, running back and forth through the same gate, and multiple people sprinting in different lanes. Some systems might also include a timing switch sensor mat to use for vertical jump testing.

When you are looking for a system that meets your budget, keep in mind that you are going to be recording a large volume of data. You will need a timing system capable of storing that data until you have the chance to download it and analyze the results. It is not going to be helpful to find you lost the data from part of your workout because you exceeded your storage.

You will find you have a choice between gates that work with single beams or multiple beams. There are pros and cons to each. The single beams are easier to set up, but anything breaking the beam is going to result in the recorded time. This can give you a false time if an athlete's arm breaks the beam first rather than the torso. Multiple beams are more accurate since all the beams have to be broken to mark the time, but they are more difficult to set up and align. Again, see what fits your needs and budget.

The same is true when deciding between a wire or a wireless system. With wires, you are limited by their length, and they handicap you if you want to set up a system of gates. The wireless gates can be placed anywhere within range, and you can easily arrange them in many types of configurations.

What it comes down to when deciding what you want to use is that you want reliability, ease of setup, and to be operable in your weather conditions. The goal is to have a timing system that will help you and your players. By running through several checkpoints, you can easily determine how players accelerate, maintain speed, and if they slow down near the end. Let's say you have set up a series of gates for a 30-meter sprint. With accurate measurements along this short route, you can address where an athlete needs to improve. He might need a more explosive start to accelerate quicker. You might discover he slows significantly halfway through and you have to train for more speed endurance or max velocity speed. What it comes down to is that if you do not have an accurate way to measure his running ability, you cannot be specific about what areas need work.

You can also utilize external metrics to track your players by monitoring them constantly while playing. We talked in the previous chapter about how you can do this with a player's heart rate, but it is also possible to track how well a player is moving with a Global Positioning System (GPS).

For sports, this technology consists of a small harness a player wears containing a GPS chip. With it, a strength coach or assistant coach can track how a player moves in practice or a game. GPS and similar type systems can track and provide data on the speed of movement during a practice or game and can show if a player is slowing down. Conversely, you might find a player who is unusually fast or strong that day, and you can make her the center of the action. This can prove to be an invaluable tool when deciding on what players to use in a game and how best to utilize them.

For us in hockey, we can fine-tune the information we gather. We can look at how each player moves in a period and break that down per shift on the ice. This technology allows us to chart when a player is first showing signs of fatigue as well as his recovery rate. When we identify these areas, it helps us figure out the appropriate amount of stress to place the players under during practice. This allows a player's body to prepare itself for game-time stress. After all, the body only knows stress and response — it does not matter if the stress is in a game or practice.

Another example is if you work with a soccer team. Have your players wear a GPS harness under their uniforms. You can quickly see that maybe your star player is not running as fast as usual. It looks like she is giving 100 percent, but it is just one of those days where something is a little off. Of course, the player is telling you that she is fine, but you can track the difference. You can now change your strategy where you might have your second-best player, who is performing at her peak, in a position to better help the team to score. The same principle can work with almost any sport.

Other technologies often incorporated into these harnesses are accelerometers and gyroscopes. These devices have two components: a mechanical movement-sensing device and a microchip that interprets signals from the mechanical device. Advances in science enable devices to be packaged together so that there is a single sensor that can record the movement of an athlete in various dimensions. This is quantifiable data that gives the coach or strength and performance coaching staff additional information to monitor the player.

Speed is important in almost any sporting competition, but there is more a player needs than that. In most games, a player needs to stop and start, make quick turns or movements, and be able to perform different skills where quickness and crispness are as important as speed. By having these type of monitoring devices, you have a clearer concept of a player's performance during a game or practice. You can show the player where she excels and where training needs to be directed to improve weaknesses. For example, a player might be fine sprinting or skating straight ahead but is not quite as quick making a turn as she usually is. This might be indicative of a physical ailment, or an area that needs more emphasis in practice. Whatever the reason, you know there is an issue, and you have the data to verify it so you can look for the solution.

All of these metrics are tools to help athletes improve their fitness and ability. Just as you want a player to practice consistently, you need to use this information constantly. It won't help to use it when it is brand new to you, but then gets lost as time goes on. Information is as much of a tool to use as a pitching machine or the equipment you have in the weight room. We want to help you make your toolbox bigger as you aspire to make your players and team better.

Gold - Silver - Bronze

Gold - Full Position Tracking/ Movement System

Similar to team Heart Rate Systems, team External Tracking Systems provide a wealth of data on all individuals within a team setting, both in real time and in retrospect.

- Kinexon Sports
- Catapult Sports
- STATSports
- STATS SportVU

Silver – Wrist-worn activity tracker/Fitbit type tool

Many "activity trackers" that are commercially available can not only measure heartrate, but can also track basic movement parameters such as steps, distance, and even things like elevation change.

- Garmin
- fitbit

Bronze – Pedometer

A basic pedometer can be used to measure total mechanical work done, as well as things like distance covered.

- Pedometers USA

External Load Metrics re: Velocity Based Training

Gold - GymAware, EliteForm, 1080

External loading metrics within the weight room generally refer to "velocity based training" tools, which measure the speed of movement during an array of exercises, and can calculate various metrics such as power output and displacement.

- Kinetic GymAware
- EliteForm

Silver – TENDO

TENDO is a brand of VBT tools that provides precise and accurate data on bar speed, which can be used for program prescription, autoregulation, and tracking power development over time.

- TENDO Sports

Bronze - PUSH Band, Bar Sensei

These tools rely on accelerometer-based data to determine bar speed and provide a low-cost entry into this space.

- Push Inc.
- Assess2Perform Bar Sensei

External Load Metrics re: Timing Systems

Gold - Laser type system...Fusion, FITLIGHT

Silver - Stomp Pads, Brower Timing Systems, Freelap

Timing gates, such as those made by Brower or Freelap, provide basic sprint times or splits between a pair of tripod-like receivers, which utilize infrared light beams, magnetic relays, or other similar technology

- Freelap USA

- Brower Timing

- Jawku Bluetooth Timing System

Bronze - Hand Timer

RELATIONSHIP BETWEEN MEAN BARBELL VELOCITY AND %1RM WITH POWER FOR TRAPBAR DEADLIFT AND BENCH PRESS IN DIVISION-I COLLEGE HOCKEY PLAYERS

Justin Roethlingshoefer[1], Bryan Mann[2], Jerry L. Mayhew[3], and William F. Brechue[4]

[1]Strength & Conditioning Department, Miami of Ohio, Oxford, OH
[2]Physical Therapy Department, University of Missouri, Columbia, MO
[3]Truman State University, Kirksville, MO
[4]A. T. Still University, Kirksville, MO

ABSTRACT

The use of velocity-based training (VBT) has become common for prescription of exercise load in recent years. As research translates from laboratory to practice, some unknowns still exist. Most notable is the fact that most exercises have been performed in rigidly controlled environments, typically using a Smith machine to eliminate extraneous motion. It would be beneficial to determine if employing typical weight room exercises produces similar relationships between percent one-repetition maximum (%1RM) and mean bar velocity (MBV). PURPOSE: To determine the relationship between MBV and %1RM for free weight bench press (BP) and trap bar deadlift (TDL). METHODS: NCAA Division-I hockey players (n= 22, age= 21.0 ± 1.5 yrs, height= 182.9 ± 7.3 cm, weight= 86.2 ± 7.3 kg) performed a standard progression to establish 1RM for each exercise. A portable accelerometer was used to measure MBV at selected %1RM between 60-90 %1RM for each exercise. Multiple repetitions were performed at each %1RM, and the best MBV from each set was utilized for analysis. BP was performed with a self-selected grip using a standard free-weight bar. TDL was performed by standing to an erect position as fast as possible while maintaining a straight back. Mean power (MP) was calculated from load and MBV. RESULTS: The correlation between MP and MBV was significantly higher for BP (r = 0.93) than for TDL (r = 0.83). The slope and intercept for the BP (MP = 618.1 MBV + 81.6) regression equation were significantly less than TDL (MP = 999.3 MBV + 284.9). The correlation between %1RM and MP was significantly higher for BP (r = 0.80) than for TDL (r = 0.57). The slopes for the regression equations of BP (MP = -7.21 %1RM + 908.0) and TDL (MP = -8.48 %1RM + 1468.8) were not significantly different, but the intercept for the BP regression equation was significantly less than for the TDL regression (908.0 and 1468.8, respectively). For every 10% increase in %1RM, MBV decreases linearly by 0.13 m/s for BP and 0.11 m/s for TDL. CONCLUSION: MBV appears to be a more accurate predictor of MP than %1RM for both BP and TDL free weight exercises in college hockey players. PRACTICAL APPLICATION: MBV can be utilized to determine appropriate training loads (%1RM) in each exercise investigated. MBV appears to be an effective means of accounting for the individual differences and assessment of daily status when determining the maximal training stimulus.

INTRODUCTION

- Velocity-based training (VBT) has emerged as the premier technique for prescribing training loads.
- The strict confines of the laboratory are now being translated to the field setting to improve training.
- Thus, it would be beneficial to utilize a typical weight room exercise to evaluate strength of the relationship between percent one-repetition maximum (%1RM) and mean bar velocity (MBV).

PURPOSES

The purpose of this study was to determine the relationship between MBV and %1RM for free weight bench press (BP) and trap bar deadlift (TDL) in college hockey players.

METHODS

- NCAA Division-I hockey players (n= 22, age= 21.0 ± 1.5 yrs, height= 182.9 ± 7.3 cm, weight= 86.2 ± 7.3 kg) performed a standard progression to establish 1RM for BP and TDL.
- A portable accelerometer was used to measure MBV at selected %1RM between 60-90 %1RM for each exercise.
- Multiple repetitions were performed at each %1RM, and the best MBV from each set was utilized for analysis.
- BP was performed with a self-selected grip using a standard free-weight bar.
- TDL was performed by standing to an erect position as fast as possible while maintaining a straight back.
- Mean power (MP) was calculated from load and MBV.

RESULTS

- The correlation between MP and MBV was significantly higher for BP (r = 0.93) than for TDL (r = 0.83).
- The slope and intercept for the BP (MP = 618.1 MBV + 81.6) regression equation were significantly less than TDL (MP = 999.3 MBV + 284.9).
- The correlation between %1RM and MP was significantly higher for BP (r = 0.80) than for TDL (r = 0.57).
- The slopes for the regression equations to estimate mean power for BP (MP = -7.21 %1RM + 908.0) and TDL (MP = -8.48 %1RM + 1468.8) were not significantly different.
- The intercept for the BP regression equation was significantly less than for the TDL regression (908.0 and 1468.8, respectively).
- For every 10% increase in %1RM, MBV decreases linearly by 0.13 m/s for BP and 0.11 m/s for TDL.

CONCLUSIONS

- MBV appears to be a more accurate predictor of MP than %1RM for both BP and TDL free weight exercises in college hockey players.
- The SEE decreased from 43 W (BP) and 102 W (TDL) to 27W (BP) and 76 W (TDL) as the MBV decreased from 0.62 to 0.20 m/s.

PRACTICAL APPLICATION

- MBV can be utilized to determine appropriate training loads (%1RM) in each exercise investigated. MBV appears to be an effective means of accounting for the individual differences and assessment of daily status when determining the maximal training stimulus.

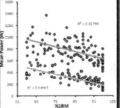

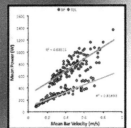

This shows how bar velocity can be used in training.

% Time >85%HR Max	Average HR Recovery	Total Calories burned	Physiological Intensity	Mechanical Intensity	shifts	time on ice	tl/min	tl/shift	Training Load
17.60	30.00	2377	3.25	2.84	30.00	21.22	14.56	10.30	308.95
5.25	26.00	853	3.39	2.88	11.00	9.56	12.64	10.98	120.83
17.23	18.00	2585	4.70	3.06	36.00	24.36	18.25	12.35	444.45
8.37	49.00	2410	3.44	3.06	31.00	22.36	16.33	11.78	365.18
11.05	27.00	2089	3.67	3.17	34.00	19.63	26.94	15.55	528.78
4.05	36.00	1904	3.19	3.57	30.00	25.47	13.95	11.84	355.27
10.26	43.00	2304	3.53	2.90	33.00	16.57	26.24	13.18	434.87
1.64	28.00	1721	2.12	2.99	22.00	14.23	14.88	9.63	211.78
11.00	11.00	2053	3.28	3.82	23.00	19.53	16.14	13.71	315.24
14.06	59.00	1897	3.07	3.52	21.00	19.22	13.16	12.04	252.86
12.13	21.00	2313	3.99	2.76	24.00	11.86	33.13	16.37	392.97
8.16	22.00	2349	3.50	2.66	15.00	10.56	37.50	26.40	395.98
19.87	31.50	1464	3.49	2.97	29.00	22.33	11.62	8.95	259.42
1.42	28.00	1305	3.29	2.78	8.00	7.22	26.80	24.19	193.49
-	-	41	1.20	3.07	28.00	19.22	15.24	10.46	293.00
15.73	21.00	2496	3.77	3.19	27.00	23.20	16.94	14.56	392.99
10.03	23.00	2239	3.43	2.38	24.00	13.52	22.42	12.63	303.07
-	-	-	-	3.01	30.00	20.78	11.79	8.17	245.00
-	1.00	804	3.48	1.00			#DIV/0!	#DIV/0!	302.00
26.84	4.00	2996	6.01	1.52	1.00	60.00	9.39	563.14	563.14
11.45	26.58	1905.30	3.46	2.86	24.05	20.04	#DIV/0!	#DIV/0!	333.96
6.70	14.41	728.40	0.93	0.64	9.37	11.03	#DIV/0!	#DIV/0!	109.99
18.16	40.99	2633.71	4.40	3.50	33.42	31.07	#DIV/0!	#DIV/0!	443.96
4.75	12.18	1176.90	2.53	2.22	14.68	9.02	#DIV/0!	#DIV/0!	223.97

An example of how we quantify external vs internal loading on our athletes.

GYMAWARE UNIT VELOCITIES (AVERAGE & PEAK)		
EXERCISE SELECTION	AVERAGE VELOCITY	PEAK VELOCITY
OLYMPIC STYLE LIFTS:		
SNATCH PULL - HANG	1.3-1.45 m/s	
SNATCH PULL - GROUND	1.4-1.81 m/s	
CLEAN PULL - HANG	1.15-1.38 m/s	
CLEAN PULL - GROUND	1.25-1.46 m/s	
STRENGTH LIFTS:		
BALLISTIC (POWER)	>1.0 m/s	> 2.0 m/s
DYNAMIC (SPEED-STRENGTH)	.8 - 1.0 m/s	1.3-1.88 m/s
DYANAMIC (STRENGTH-SPEED)	.6-.8 m/s	1.1-1.6 m/s
REPETITION	.40-.6 m/s	1.0-1.5 m/s
MAXIMAL	.2-.40 m/s	.8-1.2 m/s

This is a simple example of what characteristics of the continuum are being stressed with different bar velocities.

4

Subjective Metrics

"How do you feel?" This is a simple question, right? We use it all the time. Your child or significant other comes into the room, and you can tell she is not quite right. You do not know if she is physically hurting or overly stressed about something. Since nobody is a mind reader, you ask this basic question to start finding out what is bothering the person. We use this on colleagues, friends, and anyone else we know when we think something is wrong with them. It shows concern and most of us have the compassion to help somebody we know. However, we cannot begin to help without knowing what ails them.

When you are working with your athletes, the question of "How do you feel?" takes on even more meaning. While you are certainly going to ask your players how they feel if they are injured or hurting, this question should be a standard part of everyday contact with players. It is important to know how your players are feeling. We can have all the equipment and metrics in the world to help athletes improve their performance, but an athlete knows his body better than anyone. We have to respect what they say about how they feel.

Furthermore, as you get to know your players, you can interpret their answer to this question with more and more accuracy. Player A might constantly say he feels fine. Then one day he answers in a way that is different. Instead of saying, "I feel great," he might say, "I feel crappy today." Red flags should go up as you realize he is not fine. This is where you become part detective and part sounding board. You must begin asking questions to get to the bottom of what is bothering the player. It could be something physical; she might have fought with her boyfriend. You just do not know.

The "what" does not matter at this point. Something is off, and that means "Plan A" might not be appropriate. It might be wise to switch to "Plan B." After all, the goal of any training program should be development and progress. Sometimes, it's wise to meet the athlete where they are; other times, you stick to the training plan. However, if you do not ask a player how they are doing, then you won't receive any information to determine the most beneficial training program for that day.

Athletes tend not to share when something is bothering them. If you are a strength coach, your responsibility is to the athlete and the team. If the player is physically hurting, you need to know what the problem is. It might mean a change in practice or training regime for that individual. It might mean changing the game plan because a player is not at 100 percent. An emotional issue could be just as debilitating. If a player's head is not in the game, that can have many negative ramifications for that athlete and his teammates. The reality is that stress is stress. It does not matter if that stress is physical, emotional, or relational. It is stress, and it will affect the athlete and the team.

Being able to pinpoint some major problem affecting an athlete is always a paramount concern of any strength or performance coach. An old cliché is that a player or team should run like a well-tuned automobile. Well, when something is wrong with a car, it is not always apparent what the problem is. You have to dig into what is wrong with the machine. A person is not much different. Sometimes it takes a lot of work on your part and that of an athlete to get to the cause of why he is not at 100 percent. He might not even be sure what is wrong; he just knows he is "not right."

This may strike some as being overly engaged in an athlete's life, or soft and unnecessary, or just not what a coach does. Certainly, the old school approach of the "Commander in Chief" authoritarian-based model of coaching might not agree with this mindset. However, the reality is that society has changed, athletes have changed, and people have changed. If the goal is to get the most out of your athletes — to help them develop and grow and to work towards lofty goals as a group — then it is our responsibility as leaders to ask the question. Just like any piece of data we are discussing in this book, at no point do you have to act on the information; sometimes inaction is an act of progress. We have found that at all levels, from youth athletics through pro sports, players do not care how much you know until they know how much you care. Asking how an athlete is doing, and utilizing that info to make appropriate adjustments at the right time, not only shows that you do care but also demonstrates that you have the athlete's best interest at heart. This attitude creates trust, a buy-in to your process, and makes the journey of development smoother for all concerned.

Training is all about applying stress to achieve some desired adaptation. The brain does not know that an athlete who is bench pressing is doing that as an exercise. It simply thinks there is something very heavy about to crush the body, and the body had better get it out of the way and adapt to that stress. This way when it happens again, the body can survive that threat or an even greater threat (something heavier).

The same is true of running or skating during practice or a game. The brain does not understand that you are playing football or hockey; it just thinks you are trying to get away from some predator. The brain wants to adapt and survive by making the body faster and better conditioned so that next time that tiger jumps out from behind a tree, you can get away from it.

When you apply a stimulus and allow for recovery from that stress, then positive adaptation occurs. "Stress + Rest = Development." This is training in a nutshell.

As you can see, a good strength and conditioning program is all about manipulating the stress applied to the body to achieve a specific and desired adaptation. This is why monitoring subjective measures of wellness are important. They do not target a specific adaptation. This is why you want to monitor your athletes about how they are feeling. You want to know how much stress you can apply to each athlete in a training session so that they adapt the way you need them to, without over- or under-working them.

While you want to know in general how a player is feeling every day, we are now going to show you how to break this question down into various components to help in the training of your athletes. The more detail you receive from an athlete about how they feel, the more information you can process to help that player in his training.

The problem with asking "How are you?" is that if you are in a team setting, you most likely have 10, 20, 30, or more athletes. How do you make sure you ask each athlete, detail their answers, cross reference them compared to their past responses, and recognize the red flags? The key is to utilize a subjective questionnaire. It is still important and necessary to verbally ask the question, but a questionnaire completed by the athletes creates a more formal and recordable way to systematize this process. In a large group, this also allows you to target the few individuals who report significantly low scores so that you make sure you prioritize a conversation with the right individuals.

Players are not going to volunteer a great deal of general information if you only ask how they are doing. However, you can train athletes to relate details once you teach them what you are going to be asking on a daily basis. These might be questions on how much water they drank, how many hours of sleep they had the night before, what kind of mood they are in, if there is any soreness anywhere, etc. When you have specific questions like this, you will be able to start tracking a great deal of data on every athlete. It gives you another source of information to review if any athlete's performance wavers or if he has an off day in practice or a game.

When you have this information and can relate the data back to game performance, you are establishing an ideal blueprint for each athlete. You know how he felt when he was executing well and the opposite when he had a bad game. By tracking these small things, you can help a player improve his confidence. Sometimes it is the small things you can show a player that will make a difference in his performance.

As you have read so far, there is technology available for measuring so many facets of an athlete's abilities. We will touch on them soon, but first, we want to share a very low-tech method that will give you useful information when monitoring your players. A Wellness Questionnaire is an easy way to assess your players. It trains them to be conscious of common functions they perform daily, which are just as important as the weights they are lifting or the drills they are running.

Sleep Quality	Level of Fatigue	Muscle Soreness	Mood	Stress Level	Hours of Sleep
3	3	3	4	4	4
3	3	3	4	3	4
5	5	5	4	5	3
4	3	3	3	3	4
4	3	3	4	3	4
4	3	4	3	4	4
4	3	3	2	3	3
3	3	3	4	4	3
4	4	4	3	4	5
4	3	4	4	4	4
4	4	4	4	4	4
4	3	3	4	4	4
4	3	4	4	4	4
4	4	4	4	4	4
4	4	5	4	4	4
4	3	3	4	3	5

*Wellness data color coded to illustrate player
responses relative to their own norms.*

Using such a questionnaire enables you to gain insight into an athlete's subjective readiness. It helps a performance or sports coach pinpoint the emotional or psychological state of an athlete such as the mood he is in or his excitement for training. Physiological information such as muscle soreness, the quality and duration of sleep, and basic nutritional information such as "Did you eat breakfast?" or "How much water did you drink?" are also gathered. Any section of this data is an indicator of a player's well-being. It is a more comprehensive answer than a player telling you that he "feels fine."

Wellness Questionnaire			
History	5d Avg	Latest	Trend
Sleep Quality	3	4	+1
Hours of Sleep	4	4	0
Level of Fatigue	3	3	0
Muscle Soreness	3	4	+1
Stress Level	4	4	0
Mood	3	3	0
Are you Hurt or Sick?	0	0	0

Individual trends, including a rolling five day average.

While there are plenty of standardized, peer-reviewed, and time-tested variations of the wellness questionnaire, consistency and brevity are probably the most important components of a questionnaire. If it's too long, athletes will get weary of the time it takes to fill it out, and the data will be overly detailed for the coach. Paralysis by analysis will tend to occur. At the same time, consistently administering the questionnaire will build the habit of mindfulness on the athlete's part, and provide a robust data set that a strength or performance coach can evaluate.

The questionnaire is something you want to give the players at the start of training camp. With any measurement, you want to establish a baseline. When you know how much a player sleeps or eats when not training hard, it gives you a reference point as the season progresses.

For example, it is not good if an athlete sleeps less when he is going through multiple practices and games. It may be a sign of overtraining or an athlete's ability to cope with the stress and pressure of training and competing if he is suddenly unable to sleep after going through multiple practices and games. You want an athlete getting sufficient rest and time for the body to heal. Sleeplessness has a myriad of reasons behind it, and you can work with the player to get to the bottom of it.

Once you have a player's baseline, the next step is to make answering the questions a routine part of training. Whether you have the player fill out the questionnaire daily, three times a week, etc., depends on your program. The important point is to make it part of a player's regime as much as hitting the weight room on specified days. Again, this is all for the athlete's benefit. It helps the coaches and trainers tweak their practice schedule or intensity of what they put the players through. For example, if you have a player complaining of more soreness than usual, you might have to modify his routine for a day or two. If players indicates that they are exhausted, then it might be necessary to adjust and deviate from the original practice plan, implementing a lower intensity session for a day. You can figure out things like that when you know the specifics on how your players are feeling.

Here are some example questions you can include on an athlete questionnaire to learn more about his physiology, training intensity, and load:

- How many ounces of water did you drink yesterday?

- On a scale of 0 to 10 (with ten being "extremely well-rested"), rate your level of rest before today's training session.

- Were you physically able to complete all sets and reps of the prescribed loads in today's training session?

- On a scale of 0 to 10 (with ten being "extremely satisfied"), rate your level of satisfaction with your performance in today's training session.

Making this a regular demand on athletes helps them become more aware of their bodies. Let's face it, players, especially young players, do not think a great deal about how their physiological functions affect their play. These three things are foundational to physical wellness: eating, drinking, and sleeping. They become even more important when an athlete pushes his body to reach its highest level. By constantly reporting on these three activities, a player becomes more conscious of them. Instead of only thinking about it when answering the question, a player will be more aware of what he is doing to his body during the day. He will also see how these activities affect his physical condition. A player might learn that whenever he eats a cheeseburger and fries, he feels more lethargic when going to practice or playing in a game. Likewise, the player can see that not sleeping for as long as usual has a direct bearing on his performance. The more he learns about his body, the more likely he will be to take the proper steps to maintain optimal health and fitness.

You need to gather this information from your players consistently. Data collected just for the sake of collection, without explanation or action, is what turns athletes off from performance science. On the contrary, if the athlete understands the "why" behind what you are asking him to do, and he knows that the information will affect his training, then he will be much more likely to buy into the process, provide accurate information, and take an active interest and ownership role in the program.

Education is a powerful tool. Most athletes are motivated to improve in their sport. Sometimes, they do not immediately understand the connection between training and their actions and habits outside of their sport. By teaching the athletes the "why" behind what you ask them to do, and relating the information to their own personal goals, they are much more likely to take personal accountability for their development.

As with any data accumulation, all the information will not benefit coaches unless a disciplined charting method is part of the process and the results are shared with the performance and strength coaching staff. Taking the sleep example from above, you would not know the correlation between the amount of sleep to performance if you did not chart it and pick up on the trend. What you discover will help prepare an athlete to compete, indicate potential red flags that might reveal overtraining, and provide valuable teaching moments to players about their physiology. As with monitoring any phase of an athlete's performance, these subjective metrics need to be carefully recorded and analyzed.

As you probably realize by now, the different monitoring methods we talk about utilizing with your athletes are very beneficial on their own. However, do you recognize the significance of when you utilize your entire bank of data on a player? By keeping track of an athlete's general condition, you can often see a correlation on how he performs in training, practice, or a game.

A very simple example illustrates this. You have been monitoring Player A's intake of water during the day for several weeks now. Your data shows that he drinks anywhere from 32–64 ounces of water a day. You take that information and match it up with the player's heart rate data and his load metrics in the weight room. What you can quickly discover is that on the day he does not drink as much, or perhaps on the day after, his resting heartbeat might be faster than normal. His performance in the weight room might be a little below par. Though the difference in those measurements could be nominal, it is enough to warn you and the athlete that he needs to keep up his hydration at the high end to optimize his performance. This not only creates an opportunity for the coach to influence performance in the short term by making sure the athlete remains hydrated but also creates a chance to educate the athlete on the importance of hydration. It is one thing to tell the athlete that a small decrease in hydration will have a large impact on performance; it is quite another to illustrate the reality by showing him the data.

It might not always be this simple to discover cause and effect between what a player is doing outside of structured training and his performance. However, when you have the pertinent data, you have the information to decipher what a player needs to do to perform at his best. You might have to do some detective work because it could be a combination of physiological or psychological causes affecting performance. The bottom line is you have a wealth of information you can study.

Gathering an athlete's information can be as low tech as having the simple pen and paper subjective questionnaire for the players to fill out daily. Here is where coaches, trainers, and players begin to understand trends in their training that might not be evident to the naked eye. You can even set up one of these questionnaires online for free using Google Docs so that your athletes receive their daily questionnaire in their inbox each morning, and the results automatically come back to you on a Google spreadsheet.

If you want to become more tech savvy and have the means to do so, you can set up a questionnaire on an app or find an established one that provides the information you need from a player. All athletes have to do to is log onto their smartphones in the morning. They can report how much sleep they got last night, their level of fatigue and soreness, their mood, and a few other basic questions. This information is digitally passed along to the keeper of the data in real time. A strength or performance coach will have a sense first thing in the morning of where his players are from a recovery standpoint. This information can be very powerful, especially when you can compare how players are reporting relative to other factors, such as their typical wellness score, the training load from previous sessions, and other factors that go into the balance of fatigue and recovery.

There are other commercial monitoring systems that you can use with your players. Devices such as Apple Watches or modified Fitbits allow athletes to input information as well as record their physical activity. Various software and hardware products are on the market that enables you to record, analyze, and display the type of information we are talking about in this chapter. The level of sophistication varies, and many of the athlete management systems provide helpful statistical breakdowns of the data, but even the most rudimentary pen and paper application has the power to be extremely beneficial. As with everything we discuss, do your research and see what fits your situation and budget.

Most of what we have talked about so far in this chapter encompass front-end monitoring. You are gathering information to determine your players' readiness before they go into a training session or practice. You are looking for indicators and red flags that will help you modify what you are putting a player through that day. You want to have a clear picture of where your athletes and your team are before they walk in the door. That way you encounter fewer last-minute surprises and you can make the pertinent adjustments promptly. As discussed, keeping track of a player's data will enable you to pick up trends affecting an athlete's readiness to practice or play.

There are also advantages to back-end monitoring, which is where you ask similar questions about how a player feels immediately after a training session, practice, or game. This information is valuable for determining the condition of the player and getting an overall sense of how the training and practices are going. For example, if a coach runs what he calls a "light practice" and all the players are completely exhausted and hurting afterward, then you need to question the condition of the athletes or the intensity of the practice. A common back-end subjective tool is the session rating of perceived (RPE) exertion scale. Often, the coach's perception of intensity does not match the players' perception. An astute coach will realize that perception is a reality, and appreciate where his players are at.

The bottom line of both front and back-end subjective monitoring of your players is that you want to know how your players are doing. Whatever your players tell you is going to give you a complete picture of their condition. Think of one of your players as a pencil sketch. When you use tools like heart rate monitoring or external load metrics, you are coloring in some of the lines. By having your player relate his subjective information to you, you are filling in more of the player. As a strength or performance coach, the better you know your players, the better you can help them develop and perform. When you do this with each member of the team, the potential for that team to improve will increase exponentially.

We believe the lesson here for anyone who helps an athlete develop is to be aware and to listen. All of the monitoring and techniques we talk about in this book are very helpful. It is also important not to get so bogged down with metrics that we forget to simply look at and listen to an athlete. A player is going to know his body. Most athletes will err on the side of saying they are okay, even if they are not quite at 100 percent. One of the jobs of a coaching staff is to know if a player is doing as good as he says. In the heat of a game, you want to know if a player really is "fine" as he says, or if something is wrong. It is only through working with them in all phases of training, including these subjective metrics, that you can make intelligent deductions about how a player performs. You have the information to realize that if a player gives his all for several straight minutes during a game, then you need to rest that player for a few minutes.

Our lessons in this book are organic. Each individual concept we present is very good on its own. However, when you bring all these ideas together, you are evolving into a better coach or strength coach by assisting your players to reach a higher level of performance and readiness. If you get nothing else out of this chapter, make sure you actively listen to the answer when you ask, "How ya feeling?"

Body vs Past 30 Days

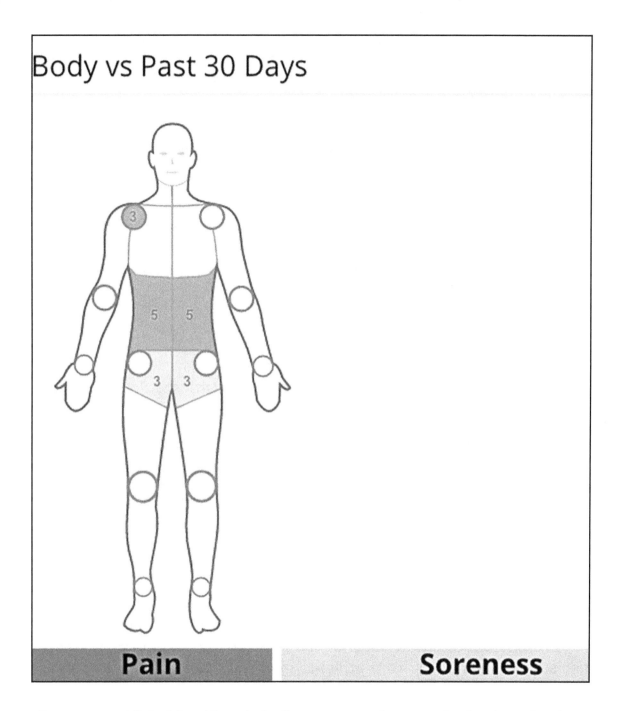

Pain **Soreness**

Soreness and Pain identifiers help flag concerns for more in-depth evaluation.

Gold - Silver - Bronze

Gold - Athlete Management System
Wellness Questionnaire

A web-based AMS allows for digital access to applications such as wellness questionnaires and session RPE scales, as well as analytics of the data, graphs and other visuals, and inter-team communication, video and link sharing, etc. These are often accessible via smartphone app, as well as on the web.

- CoachMePlus

- Kinduct

- Human 2.0 by Shift Performance - ARM (Athlete Recovery Management System)

Silver - Google Docs Emailed Wellness Questionnaire

Free online services such as Google Docs and Excel Online allow deep levels of customization with a little bit of work on the back end but are very powerful tools for collecting information and accomplishing analytic interpretation of the data.

Bronze - Pen and Paper

Pen and paper based questionnaires allow a quick and easy way to get subjective metrics from athletes, and help to foster an in-person, real-time dialogue around the data.

5

Power Enhancement

Part 1 - Jump Profiling

Have you ever observed a child's growth from a baby to a two-year-old? A naturally developing little boy or girl goes through various stages of mobilization. First, they wiggle and roll around on the floor to get from point A to point B. Then they discover how to get up on their hands and knees and crawl. This is a watershed moment for any parent as they can never assume again that their child will be on the spot they left them. Then every child's monumental moment — taking the first step. The funny thing is that it might take the average child an entire year to take that first step, and then within a week that same child is running and jumping...and jumping... and jumping.

When it comes to athletes, jump testing is second only to power testing in which coaches will measure them the most. It is an acceptable assessment of an athlete's explosive ability. Performing variations of jump tests are relatively easy and require limited energy output from the athlete. This is an important consideration as you do not want to detract from the player's ability to give his best effort in required training or during practices.

Keeping track of a player's jumping ability is another piece of information that helps chart his progress as an athlete. With this test, we want to track fatigue and see if the player is stronger during the season. To keep track of a player's improvement, we use a simple formula: Power + Force Acceleration (F=MA force is mass time acceleration). If you are moving your body weight faster or higher, you know your power is going up. Power is only able to increase with a surge in either acceleration, or in this case, mass.

Jump testing is a good tool to help trainers and coaches rate an athlete's progress in the long-term power development of a training program. It is also helpful for getting a point across to an athlete. It can confirm whether the training routine the athlete is using is working based on the measurable results of the different jump tests. Conversely, if the jump tests level out or regress, you and the athlete know you need to modify the training schedule for achieving better performance. As a side note, when you are posting your players' results, the competitive nature of the athletes comes out, and players will concentrate harder at the test to outjump their teammates.

As we said, at its core, jump testing measures the explosive ability of an athlete. Being able to jump high might not indicate any other athletic ability. The test does not necessarily indicate technical ability in a particular sport, but it shows the person has the physical potential to perform at a certain level. Jump testing is looking more at an athlete's power than his strength. Although strength is an important quality that will in some ways dictate power output, it is not the only quality. With jump testing, we are looking more at the power side of the force equation.

An athlete's jumping ability is another valuable tool to determine if he is ready to return to playing after an injury. When you have a baseline to measure against, a trainer or coach can evaluate a player's output to see if it is close to his "normal." If that explosive ability is not present yet, then it is probably not the time to return that player to full-time practice sessions or playing in a game. Just watching how a player is jumping and how he is getting in and out of position are key here. You want to know if rehab is complete, but also that strength levels and motor control are where they need to be before working the player back into a full regimen of workouts and practices.

Knowing where an athlete's weak links are allows more detailed and specific applications of training practices.

In a related matter, jump testing helps strength coaches, coaches, and players see a change in athletic development. This can either be in returning from an injury as we just mentioned, or in the general progress a player is making in training. When you are coaching a player to be faster, jump tests are an easy, efficient, and safe way to see if an athlete's lower body power is improving, as well as the central nervous system. With the variations of tests, you can also determine if one leg might be weaker than another and develop training regimes based on that information. There is a functional asymmetry between both limbs, and you can develop an appropriate training plan if there is a marked difference in power between the two legs.

For the jump tests to give you the data you want, you need the correct equipment to do the measurements. The first type we are going to talk about is force plates. As the name suggests, they precisely measure the force applied on the contact surface by strain sensors. In its simplest form, an athlete jumps into the air off the plate and lands back on it. The equipment measures the force applied to the ground to create an upward movement of the body. Force plates can also measure the comparative strength of the right and left leg. The information you obtain from force plates can help performance coaches and medical staff arrive at important decisions on the rehab progress of an injured athlete.

See Appendix Image on Page 144

Force plates are at the high end regarding the price for equipment. They tend to be more applicable for elite athletes due to the price tag and the importance of the athlete being able to replicate his jump motion each time. A deviation in the mechanics of the jump will create vastly different metrics, and these can be very important to understand. However, if the mechanics change from jump to jump simply because the athlete is a novice and has a low technical skill level, then the information put forth by the force plate will not be accurate. This is an important consideration as any variation in the takeoff or landing is going to skew the measurement. While this is true with any method you use to test jumps, it is especially important with force plates. You want a player's technique when testing to be as identical as possible from one jump to another.

Contact mats are a more inexpensive solution and used by high schools, colleges, and even at the professional level. Contact mats use a simple equation utilizing displacement of mat contact to determine jump heights. The information is not as accurate as with force plates since force is not one of the measurements here. However, they do provide data on contact time, or how long an athlete is in contact with the ground in jump tests such as the drop jump, and this particular metric can provide valuable insight into how an athlete produces power. That does mean a player can alter the results by changing how he lands. A performance coach needs to closely supervise jump tests on mats to make sure athletes are performing properly. Still, contact mats give you results you can use, and the price fits most budgets.

A simple device for testing vertical jump height is the Vertec. It consists of a base with an adjustable upright pole that supports colored vanes spaced one-half inch apart that rotate when touched for easy measurement. The test takes some skill and timing for an athlete to jump and reach to his maximum height, but it gives you an accurate indication of a player's ability to do that if he performs the jump properly. Another benefit of this tool is that it can easily be used to measure the height of "approach jumps," which are common and an important test in basketball and volleyball.

As with all training aspects we talk about in this book, there are different types and makes of equipment to measure jumps. A coach or trainer should have an idea of what they want to measure in a player's jumping ability. You need to research what fits your program and budget to choose the right equipment.

Aside from testing for pure height and reach in a jump, one of the metrics you want from a jump test is an athlete's reactive strength index (RSI). This metric illustrates how a player produces power. An athlete can spend a long time on the ground to conserve muscle motor units and produce concentric muscular force, or they can rely on the stretch-shortening cycle to produce power via stored elastic energy. Optimally, they will do both to make the best use of the combination.

According to scienceforsports.com, there are three common methods to calculate the performance of the RSI test. These are:

- *Method 1: RSI = Jump Height / Ground Contact Time*

- *Method 2: RSI = Flight Time / Ground Contact Time*

- *Method 3: RSI = Jump Height / Time to Take-off*

*Jump height is an estimate of the height change in the athlete's center of mass. Jump height is best measured using the velocity data from a force platform. This can be calculated using the following formula: Jump Height = 9.81 * (flight time) 2 / 8*

Flight time is quite simply the total time the athlete is in the air during a jump — from when they break contact with the floor, to when they first touch down upon landing. This is often measured using a jump/contact mat. However, results can be easily influenced by body position during take-off and landing. For example, if an athlete bends his legs during flight, this can alter the results and affect the accuracy of the test.

Time to take-off includes the eccentric and concentric phases of the stretch-shortening cycle.

Though both jump height and flight time can be measured directly and accurately, numerous professionals prefer to use flight time as opposed to jumping height because it is easier to obtain and less time-consuming. It makes little difference which calculation you use since jump height and flight time are strongly correlated as both are a straight mathematical derivation.

If using a force plate, it is better to use jump height based on ground reaction forces as this has been suggested to provide a more valid RSI measure. If no force plate is available, then using flight time calculated from a contact mat also works well and is often used in research.

There are different types of jumps you can have your players perform. Each variation will provide a different context. Taken collectively, you will have a more nuanced understanding of a player's strengths and weaknesses regarding his force application strategy than just one variation on its own. The countermovement jump is the typical jump to determine explosive power. Because of the utilization of an arm swing, the CMJ has an upper body element. It also utilizes some degree of the stretch-shortening cycle since the athlete "counters" the downward movement of the initial phase of the jump. This type of jump is also referred to as a long contact or long stretch shortening jump, vs. a drop jump, which has a much quicker countermovement and is often referred to as a short contact or short stretch-shortening cycle jump.

The NCM, or non-counter movement, is a jump that eliminates the stretch-shortening cycle. Hands are kept on the hips for the jump, which cuts down on the upper body movement. This leap starts out with the knees bent and the thighs parallel to the floor. The NCM provides information on an athlete's ability to produce force only from a concentric muscular action.

A single leg vertical jump provides a strength coach or performance coach with data on unilateral power development and force application, as well as left/right asymmetries. Almost all team sports are unilateral in nature. Determining the ability of each limb to produce force and create movement is important. If there is a huge difference in the force production and/or force absorption between each leg, the risk of injury increases. By assessing single leg vertical jump using a hands-on-hips technique to focus on unilateral lower body power, we can determine if any significant injury potential and/or performance detriment exists. You want to have a bilateral leg landing to avoid the risk of injury. This also assures that the jump is of maximal nature.

An even more in-depth layer of analyzation would be to utilize the force plate to measure and assess the landing ability and characteristics of each limb when landing unilaterally. Aside from using the "eye test" or use of video to determine landing strategy, the eccentric loading data from a force plate can potentially identify neuromuscular asymmetries which may be significant from an injury prevention point of view.

The drop jump has the athlete stand on an elevated surface, such as a bench. The athlete begins with hands on hips, steps off the elevated surface, allowing himself to fall toward the ground. Upon landing, the athlete attempts to "rebound" back up in the air as high and as quickly as possible. This jump variation is primarily dependent on the stretch-shortening cycle. The tendons and ligaments must rapidly absorb the kinetic energy from the descent, and quickly use that to create a force in the opposite direction. This jump will provide important information about the athlete's ability to harness "elastic energy" and not only muscular force.

There are many videos on YouTube showing the correct technique for the various jumps. Study them carefully and have your players watch them so that they can master the mechanics of each test. Consistency is so important when collecting pertinent data. You want to standardize components of the test such as bench or box height in the drop jump, hands on hips to minimize or eliminate upper body contribution, and where possible, creating a specific joint angle or squat depth requirement in the NCM assessment. Doing so removes much of the "noise from the signal" and allows you to have more faith in the reliability and repeatability of your data from jump testing.

One of the most influential things that jump testing does is allow us to identify drop-offs in power from week to week. This power testing allows us to have a better picture of the fatigue level. An important consideration when conducting jump tests is to make them as simple as possible. You need to make the procedure so easy to understand that someone off the street can perform the test. As we already mentioned, deviation in jumping form is going to throw off any jump test and make the data less reliable. If you make any changes in a test, you are going to end up with corrupt data that is not going to have any relation to previous tests.

You also want to make it easy so that the athlete wants to jump. It should not take a lot of time, and the player needs to see that her performance in a jump test is as relative and as important as speed in a 40-yard dash or maximum weight lifted on the bench press. Conduct your tests so that they go smoothly and quickly for the players. Soon, you will have a wealth of data to look at over the course of a season.

Also, most athletes not only want to see the data, but they want to know what it means and how it will affect what they are doing as well. Nothing discourages an athlete more than forcing them to complete a bevy of tests and assessments, but not letting them see the results, or even worse, not doing anything practical with the information. In this all too familiar scenario, athlete motivation quickly dissipates, and data collection becomes drudgery.

You also need to keep your data collection and analysis simple. While you do not want your jump testing to take too long for the players, the same is true with strength coaches and sports coaches. There is a saying we used earlier stating "paralysis by analysis." This point is true for all the training techniques we are talking about in this book including the jump tests. Before you go into any training protocol, know ahead of time what information you want to glean from the accumulated data. Doing so will help you focus on the segment of information you believe will best help the athlete perform better. There is nothing wrong with starting with some basic information until you are comfortable with it. From there, you can expand on how much you want to gather and interpret data from any training regime.

In fact, this is probably the best way to begin to develop a sport science program. It is easy to get overwhelmed with information, even as a seasoned pro. Starting with one or two data points, making sure they are relevant, and building from there is always good advice.

As for the data, you can accumulate helpful knowledge using research-grade force plates, but you can also get a lot of information using simpler methods like the contact mats. One football team learned a lot when they observed the *absence* of data. As the season wore on, players just could not jump anymore due to the injuries from collisions and tackles. That is a good example of how jump testing helps to reduce the chance of potential injuries with the concept that you can adjust training to help reduce the occurrence of bodily damage. By beginning to notice these trends, a good performance coach will be able to make adjustments to training to minimize injuries.

Not only will the jump testing data help determine how an athlete is progressing, but it is also a great way to judge if the overall training for a team is on the right track. Whether your team sport has 12, 20, or 80 participants, you are going to immediately see if the majority of the team is scoring higher on their jumps. If so, you are working in the right direction with your program. If not, obviously you want to make some changes in your training routine. The data also reveals if the team results plateau at a certain level. If so, you might have to make adjustments to have your players do better on the jump tests again.

As an example, create a "jump profile" that identifies strengths and weaknesses in force application for each athlete. By putting each athlete into one of several "buckets," you can easily individualize your jump and plyometric training within the team setting, and without having 30 athletes doing 30 different things. As any strength and conditioning coach knows, this is a recipe for utter chaos and lack of productivity. By putting athletes in the "needs concentric force" bucket, or the "needs elastic strength" bucket, you can have several athletes at a time working in their needed area, with only small changes in team workflow from performing different types of jumps.

Like almost every aspect of training, much of the success has to do with motivating your players. If they are leaping up to catch a football or dunking a basketball, players do not even think about it; they just soar. That is a lot different than putting your hands on your hips and jumping for training purposes. A coach once told the story about a volleyball player who seemed to have a vertical leap of three inches when doing a vertical jump test, but could make herself nine-feet tall during a game!

The biggest issue with consistent jump tests is not the equipment you use or the time in practice when you conduct the tests; it is the willingness of the athlete to learn consistency in how to do the test and to put forth his best effort each time. Athletes are conditioned not to go all out if the reward is low. This is a constant coaching problem when running a practice. It is even a bigger problem in the day-to-day training of a player. It is up to coaches and strength coaches to make the jump tests an engaging experience for the players and one they *want* to do.

The nature of the tests also goes against a player's natural inclination. Rarely does a player in any sport have to jump straight up in the air from a stationary position. Basketball and volleyball might be exceptions, but even in those sports, there is usually some forward movement leading to a jump. Utilize different vector jumps that make sense for your team. Sports that require horizontal force displacement may want to use a long jump. That is what we do in hockey. We just need to have a system for tracking and have a good protocol when conducting the tests. The single leg lateral jump is also a great measure for many sports and for identifying asymmetries.

Do not be surprised if a player asks why he cannot do a running start before his jump. Since knowledge is a good thing, explain that the jump tests are designed in such a way that it is easy to repeat again and again. Taking a running approach would make the results inconclusive since it would be impossible to replicate the exact approach each and every time. An exception to this scenario might be tracking long-term development in basketball and volleyball, where approach jumps are part of the sport. However, these are probably not great tools to monitor fatigue and readiness due to the variability of the movements. Also explain to the player that by keeping the jumping technique simple, it is easier to compare the athlete's jumps with his teammates.

Players will put more emphasis on anything they can see as a direct connection to an improvement in their performance. While players realize lifting weights is a necessity, they are going to buy into doing squats a little more when they find their jump tests increasing because they understand that a higher vertical jump means a faster motor on the field. This is part of the process of the players understanding how and what the jump testing means in relation to their sport performance. Most training leads to gradual improvement, and this is one way an athlete will observe concrete results. Explaining the "whys" behind something like jump testing is much more positive than telling a player to "just do it."

Figure out a good balance for your testing program. By that, we mean you have to judge how much testing works for you. Once players buy into jump testing, their scores will improve over time the more they do it. However, there is a fine line between testing too much and the players losing interest or getting stagnant. You have to determine where that line is for motivation to stay high among the athletes.

It also does not hurt to tap into the biggest motivation for athletes — competition. Players will give you their best jumps when they know this might be one of the judging criteria in deciding who plays and who sits. If you do not make the jump tests something that counts, athletes will lose interest. They simply get tired of it. Keep that in mind for almost any training element you run for your team. The player has to believe it is worthwhile to give his best effort.

As a strength coach, you need to be prepared for conducting your tests. Write down what you want to discover from the tests, how often you test, and how you will conduct them. Have a checklist ready to make sure you cover all the important points you need to talk to the athlete about related to the tests and to record your observations and data. When it comes to jumping tests, being thorough and disciplined about it prepares you for success. Your data will be consistent, the players will know what they are doing, and you are in a better position to help the individual player and the team constantly improve.

Part 2 - Power Profiling

Various exercise bikes are staples of training rooms. You can use them as an accompaniment or an alternative to other training. They can be used for warming up or cooling down. An athlete might need to use one because an injury prevents him from doing some of his regular exercises. Stationary bikes are so much a part of training today that you see them on the sidelines of college and professional football games or somewhere in the vicinity of a hockey bench or a baseball dugout. Some players ride them when they aren't in the middle of the action to keep loose and their muscles warm.

What we want to talk about is using these bikes as a means to chart an athlete's power. As with any athletic training, metrics help rate where a person is on the power profiling chart. Developed by Dr. Andrew Coggan, who points out that "standards are available for power across different durations that represent different physiological characteristics or abilities. These make it possible to identify a particular individual's relative strengths and weaknesses based on his 'power profile.'"

This ability ensures that a rider is only comparing himself to his own past efforts. From this information, a strength coach can help devise a program customized to that particular athlete. Dr. Coggan established a chart for this purpose. He figured that estimates of power output for riders of differing abilities could be derived from actual performance by taking part in time trials. Due to the variety of athletes regarding size, strength, body mass, etc., he decided to use as a foundation the upper and lower ends of each range based on the known performance abilities of world champion athletes and untrained persons. Tests were done using available data to ensure that this concept would produce effective guidelines.

Dr. Coggan used target guides of 5 seconds, 1 minute, and 5 minutes to reflect neuromuscular power, anaerobic capacity, maximal oxygen uptake (VO2max), and lactate threshold (LT), respectively. As he further explains, "This should NOT be taken to imply that, e.g., a 1 min all-out effort is completely anaerobic (in fact, roughly 40-45% of the energy during such exercise is derived aerobically) or fully utilizes anaerobic capacity (which generally requires 1.5-2.5 min to deplete), or, e.g., that a 5 min all-out effort entails exercising at precisely 100% of VO2max. Most athletes can sustain a power that would elicit 105-110% of their VO2max for this duration. Rather, power output over these target durations would simply be expected to correlate well with more direct measurements of these different physiological abilities."

His power training levels are the standard used for determining power levels when cycling:

Zone	Name	% of FTP	RPE	Description
1	Active Recovery	<55	<2	Easy spinning; active recovery
2	Aerobic Endurance	56-75	2-3	LSD. Age group athlete IM effort, 90 min – 2 hr
3	Tempo	76-90	4-5	Brisk group ride; elite IM, age group half-IM; 20-60 min steady
4	Lactate Threshold	91-105	6-7	Includes FTP. Time trial or Oly tri effort. Int train 6-20 min, ¼ recovery.
5 (5a)	VO2 Max	106-120	7-8	Bike race surge. Int train 2-6 min.
6 (5b)	Anaerobic Capacity	121-150	>8	Crit "bursts"; train 30" – 2 min; effort very high
7 (5c)	Sprint Power	>150	10	Short, very high intensity sprints

Another method for determining power using exercise bikes is the 6-second peak power test. The test assumes a high level of basic fitness and low-risk category of cardiovascular events. This test measures a rider's highest peak power and cadence. You may find these metrics useful if sprint interval work is part of your player's regime. It is a great way to measure an athlete's progress in his training program.

Certain bikes using pneumatic equipment allow explosive movements that can replicate the speed of competition, which helps condition the muscles to fire faster. A single 2+-inch diameter cylinder on one of these machines produces up to 500 pounds of force. It comes down to science to train the brain to respond more quickly to specific demands.

Bikes also allow athletes to continue working out to a degree even if they are injured. If one of your players has a rolled ankle or a quad or hip flexor strain, a bike provides a good option for exercising safely. It could potentially be a great tool for rehabilitation as it provides safe movement with no impact on the body. It also allows the area of the injury to move and provide blood flow to the area to aid in recovery.

Training bikes are also great for metabolic conditioning as they can help break through plateaus in an athlete's training. For example, by using interval training, players can build up their aerobic capacity without losing strength and muscle mass. Athletes can also work on their mental toughness. A bike is not an easy training tool to use and can help develop a mindset to get through tough times or pain. For example, you can do 10 sets of 30 seconds at full speed with 30 seconds off. The 30 seconds of work will seem like 60 seconds and the 30 seconds of rest will seem like 10!

This equipment can also provide active recovery benefits. Increasing blood flow to different areas of the body can also benefit a player's recovery. You can get the blood flowing by going for a walk or a light jog, but a bike can be another great tool for recovery. An athlete's heart rate will pick up simply by doing a moderate rate of speed for 10 minutes.

Here is a good place to remind all performance coaches to experience whatever new equipment that you are introducing to your players. It helps you decide what works best for your program and it helps you teach your athletes the optimal way of using any equipment. Also, it does not hurt your street cred when you know what you are talking about!

Likewise, get a handle on the data any equipment produces before you use it on your players. While there are many different variations of the stationary bike and at many different price points, some level of data will be available as long as the bike has a way to measure and display work output, such as RPMs, Watts, METs, MPH, and/or time and distance.

Also, practicing on one helps you understand the practical applications of the data. It is also easier to get a feel for the information any device puts out when only dealing with a few people. Imagine if you used it right away on the 12, 20, or 60 players you train, depending on your sport. That is a great deal of information to disseminate if you have not figured it out ahead of time.

Gold - Silver - Bronze

Jump Profiling

Gold - Force Plates, 1080 system

Force plates provide a tremendous amount of data regarding jumping strategy, force application, rate of force development, left/right limb asymmetries, time-motion analysis of movement, and a host of other beneficial metrics.

Silver - Jump Mats, Velocity based tools (GymAware)

Jump mats such as the Just Jump calculate jump height via "flight time" and can also provide data on how long an athlete is in contact with the ground. These data points can be very beneficial from a global force development profile, as well as a tool to monitor neuromuscular fatigue. Velocity based tools such as the GymAware can be used to track and monitor jump height, rate of force production, and provide detailed power profiling of athletes at different loads.

- Probotics.org

Bronze - Jump and Reach system (Vertec)

Any basic "jump and reach" vertical jump system, or even a basic tape measure on the wall, will provide helpful information when combined with various types of vertical jumps when building an individual jump profile.

Power Profiling

To measure "power," you need a tool that can essentially run the formula Force x Distance / Time. This can be on a stationary bike (Watts x Miles / Time), Velocity Based Tools in the Wt. room (Load x Displacement of the Bar / Time), etc.

Gold - Watt Bike, 1080, Force Plates

Silver - Any bike that will display some type of power metric, such as Watts, VBT, rowing ergometers.

Bronze - Measuring tape for long jump, lateral bound, etc. Anything that measures power is applicable.

Note: The same formula applies...in a long jump for example, Distance x Athlete's weight = Work. It may not be possible to measure "time" in this instance accurately, but one could in the example of running 100 meters.

Using the 1080 Sprint we get metrics such as force, speed, acceleration, and can identify asymmetries.

6

Anthropometrics

In sports, we measure everything. How fast you run. How far you run. How high you jump. How much you lift. Whatever your sport is, there is something to measure. Other measurements we pay a great deal of attention to are the physical compositions of our athletes. We keep track of their height, weight, body fat, etc.

Look at the games themselves. We keep track of shots on goal, three-point shots, touchdown-to-interception ratio, earned run average, batting average, etc. If we did not have numbers as a way to tell us how an athlete or team is performing, there would not be much point in collecting data. We like to assess the performance of a player or team. In barroom conversations of comparing teams or players from different eras, out come the statistics. With a touch of our phone, we have them at our fingertips.

Anthropometrics is the study of human body measurements. Scientists and anthropologists use anthropometrics to understand physical variations among humans. As strength coaches, we use anthropometrics to monitor our players to see how training is affecting their bodies. It is also a handy metric to use when tracking how a player is coming back from an injury. Also, monitoring various anthropometric data such as body composition is an indirect way to emphasize and monitor nutrition. It is difficult and often impossible to control what an athlete eats when he is away from the team. Generally, the time athletes spend away from the rink, court, or the field greatly outweighs the time they are at practice or training. Their decisions involving nutrition, sleep, and other basic daily habits have a tremendous impact on their development. These "other 22 hours" in the day are crucial. Consistent body fat testing with strict standards emphasizes the importance of nutrition and hydration.

Let's look at a player's weight. Often weight is looked at as something you measure on a day-to-day or even a week-to-week basis. When coupled with body fat data, you can determine if an athlete is gaining muscle, losing fat, etc. However, you can determine important insights frequent weigh-ins. By weighing your players before and after practices and games, you can get an idea of a player's hydration level. You can even do such weigh-ins at halftime, or between periods or innings, depending on how your particular sport is structured.

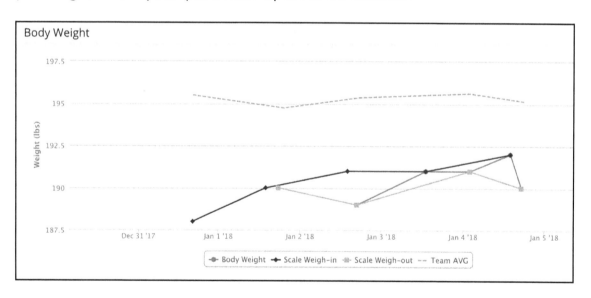

Consistent tracking of Weigh In/Weight Out captures trends in development, as well as serving as a player-educator on the importance of hydration.

Why is hydration important? Our brains consist of 70 percent fluid, and the entire body is 60-70 percent fluid. You take the water out of our bodies, and you have a few pounds of chemicals left. We can go days without eating, but only two to three days without consuming fluids. Needing to maintain a sufficient fluid level in our body is often ignored, even by our players. On a day of normal activity for a person working a sedentary job in an office, you lose 1-3 liters of fluid.

When you take in the size, activity level, and training demands of an athlete, that fluid loss soars. Science shows that a decrease in weight of just 2-3 percent from a loss of sweat can result in a 20-30 percent decrease in performance. By weighing in and out, athletes learn how much fluid they need to consume to maintain appropriate levels of hydration. A generation ago, coaches put players through hard training without allowing any water breaks. They believed it caused cramps or led to players becoming soft. There were exceptional athletes in all sports then too. Imagine what they could have done with proper hydration!

Player safety and wellness must be the priority when considering all training. There is potential for a devastating injury, debilitation, and even death due to lack of hydration. While we think of football as a fall or winter sport, most training camps at every level begin in the hot, humid days of summer. In those conditions, dehydration can occur quickly and put athletes at tremendous physical risk.

What to know about liquids in the body:

- 60-70 percent of the human body is made up of water.

- The body loses fluid through the skin as sweat, through the lungs while breathing, and through urination.

- Physical activity, heat, and humidity increase the amount of fluid your body needs to stay hydrated.

- While dehydration is a lot more common, it is possible to over-hydrate the body causing imbalances in sodium levels resulting in serious health problems.

This over-hydration is called hyponatremia, and in extreme circumstances, can even lead to death. In short, hydration is more than just water; it includes consuming electrolytes and sodium. If these levels are so diluted due to an overabundance of water-based hydration, cardiac muscle function can be impaired.

Dehydration happens during games, practices, and training when a player is losing more fluids than they are taking in. Common signs of dehydration are headaches, dizziness, dry mouth, thirst, decreased urine output, and dark yellow urine. In the case of athletes using thirst to judge their levels of dehydration, you do not want your players to get to this point. If players are thirsty, they are already suffering from dehydration; it is not a sign that dehydration is about to occur.

Here is where the anthropometrics comes in. A hydration monitor allows a performance coach to know exactly where they are with their hydration. You weigh the player before and after the game, practice, or workout. You can get an idea right away from the pounds lost to get a ballpark idea of fluid loss. When you use a hydration monitor programmed with an individual player's metrics such as sweat analysis, sweat components, sweat makeup, sweat rate, and H_2O reabsorption rate algorithms, you can determine how much fluid a player actually did lose. Then you can determine what they need to drink to properly hydrate and bring their bodies up to the proper levels of sodium, potassium, etc.

An important consideration when looking at the individual athlete is his sweat rate. Some players can jog five miles and look as fresh as before the workout. Others can run in place for five minutes in a freezer and have a puddle beneath them. The rate of sweat of a player determines how much fluid he needs to replenish. As with most thing in athletics, one size does not fit all, and you have to know your players. You can calculate the sweat rate of a player to know fluid loss and how much the player needs to drink.

According to the Korey Stringer Institute, the following steps should be followed to get the most accurate sweat rate:

1. Before the workout, ensure the athlete is hydrated (light colored urine). Being dehydrated will affect normal sweat rate.

2. Take a nude body weight before the workout.

3. Exercise for one hour (type and intensity should be similar to the conditions in which knowledge of sweat rate is needed).

4. During the one hour workout refrain from drinking fluids as this will affect sweat rate. If water is consumed, weigh the water before and after the workout to determine the difference.

5. After the workout, take another nude body weight and calculate the difference between pre and post-exercise. If water is consumed during exercise, subtract the water weight from the post-exercise weight.

Every 2.2 pounds a person loses equates to 1 liter of fluid loss (sweat loss). For example, if someone loses 5 pounds in 1 hour his sweat rate is 5/2.2 = 2.27 liters/hour. A person's sweat rate is the amount of fluid he should aim to replace during exercise. For heavy sweaters, it is not uncommon to be unable to drink everything they lose during the workout. Full replacement of fluid losses may not be able to occur until after exercise.

A general identifier to determine if your athletes are "heavy sweaters" is to take a look at the clothing an athlete wears during training after it has dried out. If there are white salt marks, it is a pretty good indicator that his sweat rate is high, and just as importantly, sodium and electrolyte loss is high. These athletes should use electrolyte-infused beverages instead of plain water.

Another component of anthropometrics is determining the body fat percentage (BFP). Mathematically, this is the total mass of fat divided by total body mass. Body fat includes essential body fat and stored body fat. Essential body fat is necessary to maintain life and reproductive functions. The percentage of essential body fat for women is greater than that for men, due to the demands of childbearing and other hormonal functions. The percentage of essential fat is 2–5 percent in men and 10–13 percent in women. Storage body fat consists of fat accumulation in adipose tissue, part of which protects internal organs in the chest and abdomen.

The body fat percentage is a measure of fitness level since it is the only body measurement that directly calculates a person's relative body composition without regard to height or weight. The widely-used body mass index (BMI) provides a measure that allows the comparison of individuals of different heights and weights. While BMI largely increases as fat increases, due to differences in body composition, other indicators of body fat give more accurate results. For example, individuals with greater muscle mass or larger bones will have higher BMIs. As such, BMI is a useful indicator of overall fitness for a large group of people, but a poor tool for determining the health of an individual, especially athletes. Many athletes, due to their higher muscle mass and general girth, will score poorly on BMI, when in reality they are in terrific shape.

Some methods available for determining body fat percentage are calipers, DEXA scans, hydrostatic weighing, or a Bod Pod.

A caliper is a tool that allows you to measure fat on a body. The 7-site skinfold test is a method of estimating body fat percentage by taking skinfold caliper measurements in three to nine different locations on the body, and then applying the results into a formula. For consistency, all measurements should be taken on the same side (usually on the right side) and by the same person. Also, a minimum of two measurements should be taken at each location. If the two measurements differ by more than 2 millimeters, do a third measurement. The skinfold test calculator then uses the average of the two to three measurements when making the calculations.

The formulas used for calculating the male and female percentages in the skinfold test calculator are as follows:

Male $BF\% = 495/(1.112-(0.00043499*s)+(0.00000055*s*s)-(0.00028826*a))-450$

Female $BF\% = 495/(1.097-(0.00046971*s)+(0.00000056*s*s)-(0.00012828*a))-450$

Variables   s = sum of 7 skinfold mm, a = age

A DEXA scan is a more sophisticated method of determining body fat. In fact, it measures bone mass, muscle mass, fat mass, and height. The procedure is simple. A person lays down on a machine with his feet together and arms by his side. He stays still for 10-15 minutes while a machine slowly moves from head to toe, centimeter by centimeter. A ray slowly covers every inch of the body. It is harmless, and no protective clothing is needed. The scanned subject feels nothing. When done, you have the necessary data. As mentioned, besides body fat, it gives you other physiology details that are good to know when comparing later scans to detect the progress of training or to monitor rehab from an injury.

Putting someone in water to determine body fat is called hydrostatic weighing. It is based on Archimedes' principle that an object displaces its own volume of water. You can use this principle to determine a person's percentage of body fat because the density of fat mass and fat-free mass are constant. Lean tissue, such as bone and muscle, is denser than water, and fat tissue is less dense than water. Basically, muscle sinks and fat floats. Therefore, a person with more body fat will weigh less underwater and be more buoyant. Someone with more muscle will weigh more underwater.

To perform underwater weighing, a person is first weighed on dry land. Next, the person will get into a large tank of water. While sitting on a special scale, he is lowered underwater and asked to expel all the air from his lungs and remain motionless while the underwater weight is measured. This procedure is repeated three times and averaged. A special calculation is then used to determine lean weight and fat weight and determine a person's percentage of body fat. By volume, fat weighs less than muscle, and pound for pound, fat and muscle each have a constant mass and displace a specific amount of water.

This method of body composition analysis is considered to be very accurate and is used to judge whether other methods are accurate. It usually is consistent, and so it can be used to measure progress. However, the person administering the test needs to understand the principles and do the calculations correctly.

The Bod Pod uses air displacement technology to determine body composition (fat and fat-free mass). A full test requires only about 5 minutes and provides highly accurate, safe, comfortable, and fast test results. It is as accurate as hydrostatic weighing, but quicker and easier to perform. The range of error for this test is ± 1 to 2.7%.

To have the best possible results, follow these simple instructions:

- No food, drink, or exercise at least 3 hours before testing.

- Use the restroom before testing, if necessary.

- Do not apply any lotions or skin creams before your test.

- Remove glasses and jewelry (if possible).

- Wear minimal, form-fitting clothing.

Sports biomechanics is another avenue of anthropometrics that allows detailed analysis of sports movements. With these results, the mechanics of movements can be improved to allow better sports performance and reduce injury risk. In training or coaching, we spend a great deal of time on the technique of our players. This encompasses how they lift weights, throw a ball, run, skate, shoot a puck, etc. Even deviating from correct form a little can greatly change the desired result or lead to an injury. As with much of what we discuss in this book, technology has reached the point where we can track and study an athlete's movements.

One of the measuring techniques is 1080 3D Mapping. As their website says, 1080 MAP is a uniquely effective and accurate test system for determining a person's fundamental ability to move. The system is based on combinations of full-body movement patterns yielding profiles that will determine what an athlete needs to do to improve mobility, stability, force, speed, power, and endurance for athletic ability. 1080 MAP is divided into three levels: movement, transformation, and performance. Movement covers mobility and stability, while transformation loads similar movement patterns to quantify force, speed, power, and endurance. Performance is the third level, quantifying performance variables.

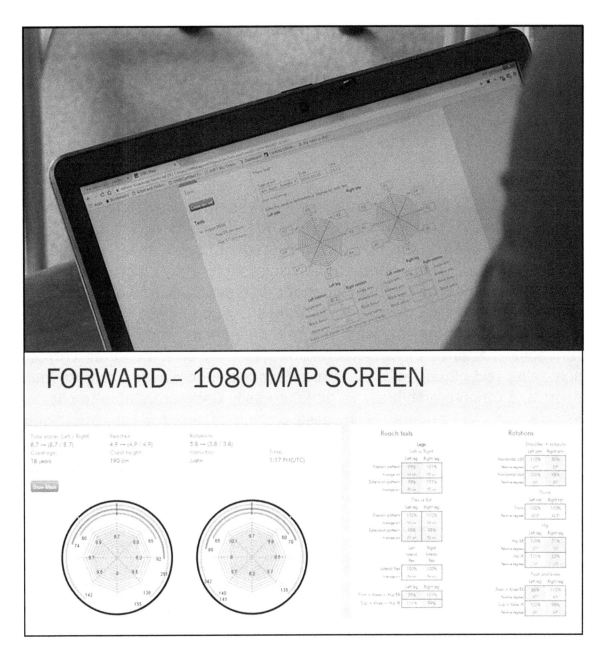

We enter mobility measurements to get a 3D look at how a player moves and his asymmetries. The second image is the final report from the mapping of a player, identifying where his asymmetries lie and where he gets his movement from.

The first level of 1080 MAP covers mobility and stability as this is the foundation of any human movement and physical performance. The goal of the testing is to determine the stable "mobility sphere." Left and right stance movements are evaluated for both magnitude and symmetry. To measure full-body three-dimensional movement patterns, the 1080 MAP is an easy to use tool. It consists of a circular test area divided by vectors. Measurements in centimeters and degrees provide the input to the 1080 MAP database.

Another service that can help with your players perfecting their movements and form is the FMS (Functional Movement Screen), which is part of the Functional Movement System. It can identify movement patterns that are fundamental to human motion and support your sport. It recognizes the true relationship that movement patterns play in health and fitness. The FMS describes principles to support the importance of movement screening, explains the role of mobility, motor control, and functional patterns in fundamental movement, and identifies correct screening techniques and common mistakes your player make in your sport and training activities. To make it easily understandable to coaches, trainers, and athletes, FMS uses scoring criteria for consistent and reliable screening results.

According to www.functionalmovement.com:

FMS uses objective and validated standards to check the movement baseline and build foundations for lifelong movement success. Therefore, certified professionals can discover the best opportunities to improve movement and identify how to train with purpose and precision for individuals to achieve their fitness, sports performance, or injury rehab goals.

The FMS is the screening tool used to identify limitations or asymmetries. It measures seven fundamental movement patterns that are key to functional movement quality in individuals with no current pain or known musculoskeletal injury.

Using FMS scoring results, movement principles are then put into action to make programming decisions and guide purpose-driven exercise selection. The FMS is that ongoing feedback tool that makes the entire training process — short-term and long-term — both effective and efficient.

The idea behind a movement screen such as the FMS is to create a baseline of foundational movement with which you can refer back to and "check your work." After an athlete progresses through a training program, the movement screen scores can be compared to earlier assessments to identify improvement from poor scores or maintenance of good scores. Movement screens also identify "red flags" in improper movement patterns, which need addressing or additional attention by the sports performance coach to reduce the incidence of future injury and to avoid adding strength to dysfunction.

As you know by now, you can pick and choose from these options and any new concepts that hit our industry according to your budget and resources. The bottom line is that monitoring your athletes with how their bodies are developing is going to pay off for everyone in the end. It is going to help the player reach his optimal performance levels. When that happens, coaches have solid players they can work with to form a winning team. Performance coaches are going to be able to fine-tune the workouts for each player more effectively. When you make some of the techniques here part of your team's routine, you will see an improvement in the performance, robustness, and stamina of your athletes.

Gold - Silver - Bronze

Anthropometrics

Gold – Bod Pod, Dexa, Hydrostatic weighing

Silver - InBody scale

Bronze - Calipers, scale

Simply by using handheld body composition calipers in either a 3-site, 7-site, or 10-site pinching system, along with basic weight tracking from a run-of-the-mill scale, body composition, percentage lean or percentage fat mass, etc., can all be easily determined.

Body Screening

**Gold - Dari Lab Biomechanical Screen/
any 3D motion capture analysis system**

Silver – 1080 MAP, Algorithmic Body Screen

Bronze - Movement Screen, FMS, SFMA

Any structured, organized, and repeatable movement screen system will provide ample information for little to no cost on athlete asymmetries, movement dysfunctions, limitations, and red flag problem areas. Tools such as the FMS and SFMA provide for accurate and detailed analysis as a first line of defense and understanding of athlete movement strategies in a standardized environment.

- Functional Movement

7

Nutrition

Jimmy Branham, CEO, The Meal Prep Co, contributed to this chapter

You are familiar with the saying, "You are what you eat." This takes on even more significance in the world of athletics. Players need to care for the vessel that allows them to perform at a higher level. As strength coaches, this is also a concern for us. For our players to take maximum advantage of their training, we want their bodies to be properly fueled and ready to go. Remember, everything discussed in this book is a holistic approach to helping an athlete develop and reach his potential. All methods can have positive results for an athlete, but it is nothing like he will achieve when your team culture incorporates *everything* into your program.

Your first concern should involve the general health of your players, including proper recovery. Educating players more about their bodies allows them to prevent diseases, deficiencies, illness, and injuries. Preventing all of these not only keeps the players in the game, but also helps them to perform at their peak.

We know that we have to start somewhere when planning our fitness goals. In a sense, we cannot bake the perfect cake without some direction or recipe. You cannot take a cookie-cutter approach to a plan for each player when everybody's genetic background is different. When sitting down and talking one-on-one with your players to focus on their past nutrition and activity level, you want to find out what worked for them and what did not. An athlete knows better than anybody else what sits well with his stomach and what does not. If milk does not digest well for a player, then you know to remove all dairy/lactose products from that player's meal plan.

Several things to consider when drawing out a nutrition plan are a basic body weight scale, body fat testing (InBody, hydrostatic dunk, pinch test), food allergy/sensitivity test, and genetic testing. All are very different in price but all very beneficial. We will discuss the different benefits of these tests and illustrate what information is necessary in designing a nutrition plan for a player.

First, it is important to determine the amount of muscle a player has since it is closely related to strength or potential strength. It also plays a huge role in how fast an athlete's metabolism is and how many calories he potentially burns at rest. After figuring out that calorie intake, you can help determine if the player needs to eat in a deficit, maintenance, or surplus manner in regards to calories. You want this to sync with the player's fitness goals. The percentage of those calories determines body composition and energy output.

As we talked about in the last chapter, a simple and cost-efficient way to determine your body fat percentage is the pinch test or a visual example. If a player is relatively low in body fat, you should start to be able to see some abdominal muscles coming in. At around 16 percent, you should start seeing the upper abs, at around 12 percent obliques come in, then below ten, we start seeing the v cut and lower abs. With the pinch test, you could use the most common formula from Jackson-Pollock with the seven measurements documented (chest, abs, thighs, and triceps) and bone density. Ideally, you can use a hydrostatic dunk or InBody test to determine a more accurate body fat percentage number.

The fat percentage number multiplied by a player's total weight gives you fat mass and lean body mass. An example would be someone who weighs in at 200 lbs and has a body fat percentage of 15. He would have 30 lbs of fat, therefore 170 lbs of lean body mass. For an athlete, this is a good percentage to target. Body fat percentage shouldn't be below 10 percent. Athletes need fat reserves for long, intense games once they tap out their glycogen reserves to avoid any muscle loss. This fat also plays a huge role in cushioning the vital organs exposed to damage with most contact sports.

Consider general physics for a moment. More mass equates to more strength and force, but ultimately muscle is the force behind that strength. Testing for body fat percentage gives you information on the estimated calorie intake to either gain, lose, or maintain the player's current body weight.

With that information alone, you can start to map out a meal plan for a player. The general rule with protein is 1g per pound of lean body mass. You can then adjust according to a player's goal and activity level. For fat loss, you want an athlete to increase protein so he can reduce the carbohydrate intake while still reaching the minimum calorie intake for that type of day. Our bodies' first preference for energy will be carbohydrates, so if we continue to fill the tank of glycogen, our body does not have any need to touch our fat reserves. When following a lean mass gaining program, you want to make more room for carbohydrates. This equates to a calorie surplus, but to keep things lean, we should always pair strength training with light cardio.

You want to counsel your players to leave room for a couple of pounds of fat gained during a muscle building program to ensure that they have a little surplus of body fat necessary to gain the most amount of muscle mass. A maintenance program is for when a player is at a prime body fat percentage, but still obviously wants to gain muscle by strength training. This program is equally challenging because an athlete still has to keep things relatively clean and accounted for to avoid fat. Most players find themselves undereating in this program because of underestimating food intake on the days of higher activity.

Here are a couple of examples of athletes with similar profiles based on their recorded fat percentages. One is on a muscle building program and the other is on a fat burning program. Both had similar goals of being at 7 percent body fat while engaging in similar high activity levels. The one wanting to gain muscle/weight was 6 foot 6 inches tall and weighed in at 172 lbs with a body fat percentage of 5.06. His daily rest day calorie intake was 2538 Kcals with 30 percent protein, 44 percent carbohydrates, and 24 percent fats. The one wanting to lose body fat/weight was 6 foot 4 inches tall and weighed in at 209 lbs with a body fat percentage of 8.47. Therefore, his daily rest day calorie intake was 2272 Kcals with 43 percent protein, 24 percent carbohydrates, and 32 percent fats. Both calorie intakes will increase day by day depending on the intensity of activity.

For all athletes, our first concern is not how they look aesthetically, but how their bodies handle a proper recovery. We want to focus our players on avoiding all injuries and illness instead of being too focused on losing a couple of pounds on the scale. You want your players to always have a full tank of glycogen for maximum energy output, especially on game days where they might be playing three to four hours. Falling into a catabolic (muscle wasting) effect often happens in long games due to not priming their bodies correctly beforehand. This might mean priming an entire day ahead of time depending on their absorption rate.

The pinnacle of human body testing is DNA genetic testing. It goes in-depth on all around health, abilities, deficiencies, sensitivities, and more. Wouldn't it be nice to know a player's genetic athletic capabilities and inherited traits so that you can fine-tune his training program? These tests are becoming a lot less of a hassle to get done. Now you can send a swab of a player's saliva through the mail straight to the laboratory for testing. You can get the results back in as early as three to five days. It would be optimum to have a player get this test at least once as opposed to a hydrostatic dunk test at least once every two to three months. Cost is significantly different since an average DNA analysis test would run around $500 compared to a $60 hydrostatic dunk test.

One of the great results you get from a DNA test is knowing what gifts your player inherited from his parents. One prime example would be physical ability or strength. A single swab of the mouth can tell you if an athlete is ever going to have what it takes to become a professional athlete. One particular trait that would increase someone's athletic ability would be eyesight. Depth perception, peripheral vision, and reaction speed are highly necessary for most athletes to reach a higher level.

For all around health, this is a fantastic test in which to invest. It can help a player avoid certain foods that are not meant for his body and introduce foods known to improve it. Knowing what vitamins and minerals a body is specifically deficient in help pinpoint where the problem is. For example, someone whose hereditary traits are known to be deficient in Vitamin D will likely show up on the test. A healthy daily dose of Vitamin D for athletes is around 5,000 IU per day. On a test, we want to aim to be around 40-50 ng/ml or higher to be optimal. Simply from knowing this, we can avoid all the side effects of being low in Vitamin D (muscle pain, bone loss, fatigue, hair loss, depression, bone and back pain, illness).

Being deficient in one simple vitamin can prevent someone from ever playing at peak performance, properly recovering, or having longevity in a sport. We can tweak our nutritional program based on these results other than simply targeting a certain calorie intake. For example, removing gluten out of someone's diet because it's known to cause inflammation in his body is a game changer, preventing heart disease, lung issues, diabetes, and arthritis.

When designing a nutritional plan around an athlete's activity level, we should pay close attention to insulin sensitivity. This is a main reason why someone has trouble absorbing proper nutrients into the muscles and getting rid of that midsection. Insulin is a hormone that helps the body stay anabolic and absorb nutrients into muscle cells, promoting fat loss.

The most common missing piece in the puzzle is water consumption. So many athletes have insane cravings due to improper water consumption and try to fill that void of dehydration with more calories. If everybody had a goal of hitting 1.5 ounces of water times their current body weight, we would all be in better shape. Take it a step further and adjust it based on an athlete's weekly physical activity (work and leisure). H2O plays a key role in every aspect of human health, wellness, and performance. Another rule of thumb is to drink 16 ounces of water before and after every meal, fitting our calories into no fewer than three to seven meals on a daily basis. This also ensures we divide our water consumption evenly throughout the day as well as calories. Carrying around a gallon of water all day does not always help if we forget it is there.

We have to teach our athletes that they absorb micronutrients through the small intestines and they have to consider their gut lining. It is important to make sure they have plenty of water to flush out the harsh toxins from some of their poor diet choices. Keep in mind that caffeine and alcohol consumption throughout the day, which work as diuretics, strip the body of more water. You need to drink enough water to counteract any caffeine or alcohol consumption.

By absorbing more nutrients during a lean mass building diet regimen, players capitalize on all of the calories they are trying to eat in surplus. This helps with minimizing fat retention, building more lean muscle, and minimizing injuries during a strength and conditioning program. Water also lubricates and cushions ligaments, tendons, and muscle fibers, which helps in aiding and preventing muscle tears or pulls (the most common injury in an athlete). This ultimately allows a player to have a better quality of sleep or rapid eye movement (REM), resulting in more natural growth hormones being released to speed up recovery and reduce cortisol levels.

For fat loss, we have to consider water pushing out not only the toxins harming the body but fat as well. Fat is lost through sweat glands and urine, so it is a good sign to see players have more sweaty sessions at the gym and a few more trips to the restroom. Also, keep in mind that fat loss diets often result in less starchy carbs, which ultimately means less water retention.

Besides veggies (which are made of 80 percent water), water is the only other unlimited item in any diet regimen. The more an athlete eats vegetables and drinks water, the better the player is going to look and feel — both inside and out. Drinking high alkaline water and having an abundance of organic veggies and fruits will ultimately prevent any and all airborne illness, free radicals, and diseases. As athletes train, they are exposed to these while also stripping the antioxidants that protect the body. You need to have your players do whatever is necessary to replenish them to stay healthy.

The most common goal for the majority of society is that everybody wants to see that weight number go down on the scale. While fat loss can be very easy, most people want to rush the process and fall under the category of "weight loss," which involves losing a lot of muscle as well. When the goal is fat loss, body fat percentage should be looked at to determine the goal. By losing muscle in the process of trying to lose fat, a person's metabolism slows down, and so does carb tolerance that puts a person ten steps backward. On the other hand, if an athlete gains a little muscle while dropping body fat, his metabolism actually speeds up as well as his carb tolerance, enabling the body to burn more calories at rest.

Building up a carb tolerance is accomplished by weight training, cardio sessions, and depletion of carbohydrates through diet. By depleting carbs, we are priming the body for fat loss by drying out the "glycogen sponge." This translates into less stored energy available so that the body has a chance to pull from its fat reserves for energy. To avoid losing muscle in the process, a player has to work at a relatively high intensity at times to stay in an anti-catabolic phase. While carbs should stay low with low glycemic levels the majority of the time, sudden spikes in insulin through natural sugars after an intense workout bring a player back to a balanced anabolic stage, ideal for muscle growth. Grabbing a protein shake and a Gatorade after a workout is actually okay, regardless of the "high sugars." Those sugars consist of maltodextrin and dextrose, which the worked-out muscles will quickly absorb and store as glycogen for later use. By separating your cardio and weight training, you will also create a greater carb tolerance.

Doing a cardio workout before the first meal of the day after fasting for 8 hours while sleeping helps tap into fat storage. You can help a player avoid any muscle loss by sipping on branch chain amino acids (BCAA) while doing cardio. BCAA is protein without the calories, helping to maintain more muscle. Muscle loss can be at a higher risk in the morning since our cortisol levels are at their highest points. Taking in some form of Omega-3 in the morning will help maintain healthy cortisol levels.

When losing fat, a player first must learn how many calories he is burning at rest. This can be measured by body fat testing and a resting metabolic rate (RMR) test. After establishing calorie burned at rest, you can increase the player's calories via carbs the days that are more active (hike, jog, light workout) by about 200-600 calories. Then pick "re-feed days" where the player would only be doing resistance training and focus on large muscle groups like legs or back. On these days you want the player to add 200-600 calories from carbs, still keeping natural sugars relatively low.

For a pre-workout meal, an athlete should eat about an hour before working out and have it well-balanced with a lean protein source, complex carbohydrates, and fats high in Omega-3. All three will be absorbed within two to four hours to help sustain plenty of endurance and keep the anabolic rate. The carbs will start to shuttle themselves into the bloodstream for use during activity.

During workouts, players need to work on keeping a balanced insulin level to sustain energy and endurance during the activity. It is a good idea to introduce a small Gatorade with BCAA to help balance the insulin level. Of course, plenty of water should follow the workout.

The post-workout meal should be the player's biggest meal. He just depleted his body of nutrients, and this meal should be consumed within two hours after activity. It should include a fast-acting protein shake (isolated, whey, or concentrate), L-Glutamine, creatine hydrochloride (750mg per 100 lbs body weight) or creatine monohydrate (5-10g), and a fast-acting carbohydrate like Gatorade, full of potassium and electrolytes.

Drink Gatorade because the sugar causes an initial insulin spike that helps shuttle nutrients straight into the muscle cells, causing an anabolic environment. Gatorade is made with maltodextrin and dextrose, which are better absorbed in the muscle as opposed to fructose in the liver. How much Gatorade consumed depends on the activity level that day, insulin sensitivity, muscles worked out, and quantity of muscle mass. Always advise avoiding fats during the post-workout meal because fats slow down the absorption of nutrients. Instead, have the player focus on getting more calories from carbohydrates to refill on glycogen. Think of protein as being the needle and carbs as the thread; they shuttle into the muscle to repair any damage before lactic acid builds up and forms scar tissue.

When you are teaching your players how to eat properly to complement all of their physical activity, for many of them, you are introducing a total lifestyle change. Eating habits are hard to change, especially depending on how a player grew up. Just as we need to do in explaining equipment, testing, and why the data we collect is important, we have to educate our athletes on nutrition and hydration. This is the fuel they put into their engine, and it is our job to teach them the best way to do so. As with everything we are discussing in this book, once they see the positive difference in their bodies, you will have devoted followers of your program.

Gold - Silver - Bronze

Gold - DNA testing, blood, or saliva

Silver - Equation based upon body type and body comp i.e. precision nutrition, macro eating

Bronze - Meal diary...nutrition education, grocery store trips

Hydration

Gold – sweat analysis, keytone variance

Silver - urine test

Bronze - Weight loss equation

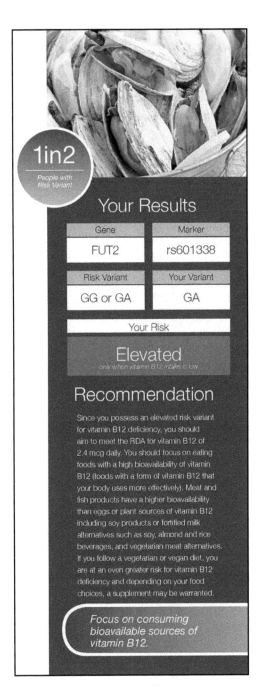

1in2

People with Risk Variant

Your Results

Gene	Marker
FUT2	rs601338

Risk Variant	Your Variant
GG or GA	GA

Your Risk

Elevated
only when vitamin B12 intake is low

Recommendation

Since you possess an elevated risk variant for vitamin B12 deficiency, you should aim to meet the RDA for vitamin B12 of 2.4 mcg daily. You should focus on eating foods with a high bioavailability of vitamin B12 (foods with a form of vitamin B12 that your body uses more effectively). Meat and fish products have a higher bioavailability than eggs or plant sources of vitamin B12 including soy products or fortified milk alternatives such as soy, almond and rice beverages, and vegetarian meat alternatives. If you follow a vegetarian or vegan diet, you are at an even greater risk for vitamin B12 deficiency and depending on your food choices, a supplement may be warranted.

Focus on consuming bioavailable sources of vitamin B12.

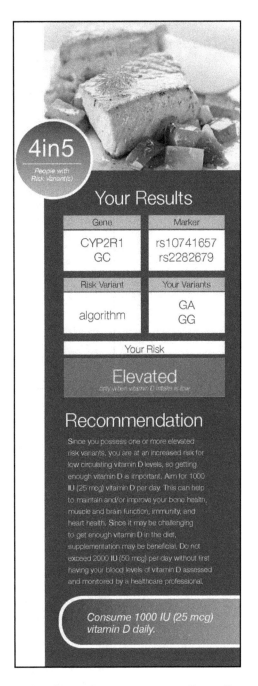

4in5

People with Risk Variant(s)

Your Results

Gene	Marker
CYP2R1 GC	rs10741657 rs2282679

Risk Variant	Your Variants
algorithm	GA GG

Your Risk

Elevated
only when vitamin D intake is low

Recommendation

Since you possess one or more elevated risk variants, you are at an increased risk for low circulating vitamin D levels, so getting enough vitamin D is important. Aim for 1000 IU (25 mcg) vitamin D per day. This can help to maintain and/or improve your bone health, muscle and brain function, immunity, and heart health. Since it may be challenging to get enough vitamin D in the diet, supplementation may be beneficial. Do not exceed 2000 IU (50 mcg) per day without first having your blood levels of vitamin D assessed and monitored by a healthcare professional.

Consume 1000 IU (25 mcg) vitamin D daily.

Food prepping is the easiest way to ensure that the proper quality of food is available when needed. Educating each athlete on the types and qualities of food they eat is the least expensive way to ensure an athlete is getting proper nutrition. Courtesy Nutrigenomix

This is a sample of what a DNA Nutritional analysis would look like.
Courtesy Nutrigenomix

Energy Balance

Energy is used to fuel all of the body's functions. A calorie is a commonly used unit of measurement to quantify energy. Energy comes from the foods and beverages consumed. The body then uses energy to complete essential processes such as digestion, breathing, brain function and maintaining a normal body temperature. The energy burned during these essential processes is referred to as the Resting Metabolic Rate (RMR), which can vary substantially between individuals. Variability in RMR can depend on differences in muscle mass, weight, age and genetics. Research shows that variation in the UCP1 gene affects RMR*. Total energy output is the sum of the RMR plus energy burned during physical activity. Consuming less energy and/or expending more energy can lead to weight loss.

* Nagai N et al. UCP1 genetic polymorphism (-3826A/G) diminishes resting energy expenditure and thermoregulatory sympathetic nervous system activity in young females. Int J Obesity. 2011;35:1050-5.

UCP1

Uncoupling protein 1 (UCP1) is found in fat tissue and is involved in metabolic processes that create energy and then release it in the form of heat. The UCP1 gene is important for regulating normal body temperature and can impact RMR. Research shows that individuals with the GG or GA variants tend to have lower RMRs compared to individuals with the AA variant. As such, they need to consume less energy to maintain regular bodily functions.

Sources of High Energy Foods

	Amount (calories)
Double patty hamburger (1)	580
Chicken Caesar salad (2 cups)	490
Pizza with pepperoni and cheese (1/2 of 12")	440
Mixed nuts, roasted (1/2 cup)	410
Carrot muffin (1 medium)	340
Avocado (1 fruit)	320
Cheeseburger (1)	320
Donut, chocolate covered (1)	270
French fries (20-25)	240
Croissant (1)	230

Source: Health Canada's Nutrient Value of Some Common Foods

Summary of Results

Nutrient Metabolism

Dietary Component	Gene, rs Number	Risk Variant	Your Variant	Your Risk	Recommendations
Vitamin A	BCMO1, rs11645428	GG	GG	Elevated	Focus on consuming pre-formed sources of vitamin A.
Vitamin B$_{12}$	FUT2, rs601338	GG or GA	GA	Elevated	Focus on consuming bioavailable sources of vitamin B12.
Vitamin C	GSTT1, rs2266633	Del	Ins	Typical	Meet the RDA for vitamin C daily.
Vitamin D	CYP2R1, rs10741657	Algorithm	GA	Elevated	Consume 1000 IU (25 mcg) vitamin D daily.
	GC, rs2282679		GG		
Vitamin E	F5, rs6025	CT or TT	CC	Typical	Meet the RDA for vitamin E daily.
Folate	MTHFR, rs1801133	CT or TT	TT	Elevated	Meet the RDA for folate daily.
Iron Overload	SLC17A1 rs17342717	Algorithm	CC	Low	Follow the recommendations provided in the Low Iron Status section.
	HFE rs1800562		GG		
	HFE rs1799945		CC		
Low Iron Status	TMPRSS6 rs4820268	Algorithm	GA	Typical	Meet the RDA for iron daily.
	TFR2 rs7385804		CA		
	TF rs3811647		AA		
Calcium	GC, rs7041	Algorithm	TG	Elevated	Consume 1200mg of calcium daily.
	GC, rs4588		CA		

Cardiometabolic Health

Dietary Component	Gene, rs Number	Risk Variant	Your Variant	Your Risk	Recommendations
Caffeine	CYP1A2, rs2472300	GA or AA	AA	Elevated	Limit caffeine intake to 200 mg/day.
Whole Grains	TCF7L2, rs12255372	TT or GT	GT	Elevated	Consume most grain products as whole grains.
Sodium	ACE, rs4343	GA or AA	AA	Elevated	Limit sodium intake to 1500 mg/day.
Omega-3 Fat	NOS3, rs1799983	TT or GT	GG	Typical	Consume between 200-500 mg per day of omega-3 fat.
Saturated Fat	APOA2, rs5082	CC	TC	Typical	Limit intake of saturated fat to no more than 10% of energy.

Weight Management and Body Composition

Dietary/ Fitness Component	Gene, rs Number	Response Variant	Your Variant	Your Response	Recommendations
Energy Balance	UCP1, rs1800592	GG or GA	GA	Diminished	Aim for an energy deficit of 650 calories/day from your calculated energy needs for weight loss.
Physical Activity	FTO, rs9939609	AA	TA	Typical	Aim for 150 min/week of cardio and at least 2 days/week of muscle-strengthening activities.
Protein	FTO, rs9939609	AA	TA	Typical	Consume 20-30% of energy from protein or 1.2-1.4 g protein/kg body weight.
Total Fat	TCF7L2, rs7903146	TT	CC	Typical	Consume 20-35% of energy from fat.
Saturated and Unsaturated Fat	FTO, rs9939609	TA or AA	TA	Enhanced	Limit intake of saturated fat to no more than 10% of energy. Consume at least 5% of energy from polyunsaturated fat.
Monounsaturated Fat	PPARγ2, rs1801282	GG or GC	CC	Typical	Aim for a balance of saturated, monounsaturated and polyunsaturated fats to meet your total daily fat intake.

Food Intolerances

Dietary Component	Gene, rs Number	Risk Variant	Your Variant	Your Risk	Recommendations
Lactose	MCM6, rs4988235	CC or CT	CT	Slightly Elevated	Limit dairy intake.
Gluten	HLA, rs2395182	Algorithm	GT	Medium	Medium risk for gluten intolerance.
	HLA, rs7775228		TT		
	HLA, rs2187668		CT		
	HLA, rs4639334		GG		
	HLA, rs7454108		TT		
	HLA, rs4713586		AA		

Eating Habits

Dietary Component	Gene, rs Number	Risk Variant	Your Variant	Your Risk/Response	Recommendations
Fat Taste Perception	CD36, rs1761667	GG or GA	AA	Typical	Your ability to sense the fatty taste of foods is typical.
Sugar Preference	GLUT2, rs5400	CT or TT	CT	Elevated	You have a high preference for sugar.
Eating Between Meals	MC4R, rs17782313	CC or CT	TT	Typical	Your tendency to eat between meals is typical.
Starch	AMY1, rs4244372	AA	AT	Typical	Your ability to metabolize starch is typical.

Hydrostatic Evaluation

Body Fat %:	8.1%	Fat Body Mass:	15.43 lbs
Lean Body Mass %:	91.9%	Lean Body Mass:	175.07 lbs
Ideal Body Fat %:	15%	Weight for Ideal:	205.96 lbs
Goal Body Fat %:	7%	Weight for Goal:	188.25 lbs

Metabolic Information

Activity Level:	over 12 hours
Maximum Exercising Pulse:	179 bpm

137 ———— fat burning zone ———— 158 ———— cardio training zone ———— 179

Calorie Intake Per Day

lose 2 lbs/week	lose 1 lbs/week	maintain	gain 1 lbs/week	gain 2 lbs/week
2429	2929	3429	3929	4429

Hydrostatic Test Data

Gender:	Male	Age:	21 yrs
Height:	73 in	Weight:	190.5 lbs
Ankle Circumference:		Resting Pulse:	65 bpm
Water Temperature:	34 °C	Water Weight:	7900 grams

This is an in-depth anthropometric analysis using a hydrostatic wiring to determine lean mass to fat mass ratios and determine athlete goals.

8

Analytics

We have talked about the various techniques we use in the sport science arena to help our athletes become the best versions of themselves. The other part of our job is providing information to the coaching staff so that they can make better decisions on how to structure practices, and on the utilization of players during games. The dilemma facing strength coaches is how to consolidate all the information we gather into a concise and usable form. When you do this, you are allowing the coach to coach. You are not stepping on his toes, but you allow the coach to see the value of your data. The more that coaches see the value and applicable use of the data, the more they will buy into what you do for the team.

Analytics is studying your data on each player and being able to extract from that information what you can to help that athlete improve. The problem that usually arises is the sense of being overwhelmed by the sheer volume of information that you accumulated. If you are new to training athletes with some of the techniques we discussed or have started working for a team that does more with its players than you are used to, remember this cliché: "How do you eat an elephant?" Answer: "One bite at a time."

In other words, you need to systematically approach the entire concept of applied sport science to your program. This chapter could be its own book, and it will in the future. For now, we want you to have a strong overview of how to use analytics in your work. We want to concentrate on two important concepts regarding analytics: how you organize your workouts and training sessions for your players, and how you work with the data you record on each player. If you take all we talked about in stages, you, the coaches, and the players are going to understand better the how and the why of what you are doing with your program.

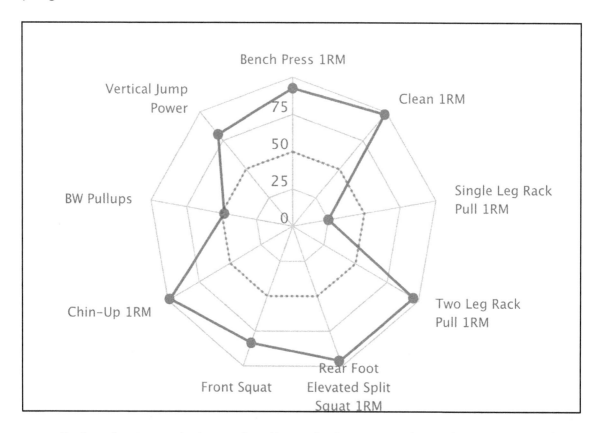

Radar charts can help to visualize relative strengths and weaknesses.

We also want to caution you against trying to do everything at once if you are new to this. Part of human nature is that we all get excited by something new that might help us in our profession. We know that the concepts and technique we talk about here are solid and we have seen the positive results. However, people can also get that "kid in the candy store" feeling. You want it all! You can do it all, but just like a child who might run through the candy store and eat everything in sight, you might get a bellyache. Or more accurately for the sports and training profession, a very big headache.

All programs are different in skill level, coaching experience, and budget. Performance and strength coaches need to sit down with the rest of the coaching staff and figure out what best works for your sport and your program. You might want to roll out the heart rate monitors first. Or maybe you have been doing your version of the jump test, but you want to upgrade your equipment to get more accurate readings.

A good rule of thumb is that once you decide what is going to be part of your training, master each element with your athletes before adding another piece. It is not like we are talking weeks or months to get a handle on something for you and the players. Some of what we talked about might only take a day or two to get the technique or equipment down pat, but you do not want you or your players getting discouraged by trying to do too much at once. Information overload can happen to players and coaches alike.

As you and the players become accustomed to the different data-centric elements that become a regular part of their training, it is important to schedule them in such a way that they are the most effective. Most people love a routine. This is especially true in sports as a rhythm develops in training camp. You then have to reset that routine when it morphs into something different during the season when the games begin. Coaches and players both thrive on the idea that if it is a Tuesday, they know exactly what is going to happen that day at training or practice.

By systematically integrating sport science, a routine and familiarity develop around the use of these tools and techniques. Avoiding the feeling of intrusion is important when asking the players to engage in assessments, data collection, or other monitoring techniques. If this becomes cumbersome, it will be much more difficult to collect what you need on a consistent basis. It will also make buy-in that much more difficult by the coaching staff and players.

There is a slight flip side of this coin, though. While routine is good, you also want to keep the athletes mentally fresh. Perhaps you can work on power one day in a different way then you did the previous time. You also want to be sure that you are doing some development work with your players every day. Monitoring and analytics need to be a part of the process, not a separate entity in and of itself.

The schedule you set up has to work with your team. We coach with different levels of hockey players. Justin works with pros and Devan with college athletes. What we establish for training during the season is different from each other due to the pros playing more games with a longer season and other considerations. If you are at the high school level, you might have limited time to use the weight room or other facilities. The bottom line is that you want to establish your training routine so that you can maximize what you have to work with for the benefit of your players.

What we want to do here is show you our typical weeks so that you can get an idea of structure. This is what works for us. We hope it helps you think about how to schedule your week. However, there is more than one way to skin a cat. The point here is that we both have a system in place that allows us to consistently and accurately collect and analyze pertinent information, as well as create a structured and progression-based training program throughout a long season.

Devan:

- Sunday - Compile reports based on data recorded from training sessions and games. The reports detail the past week and make recommendations for the upcoming week based on physiological data accumulated. For example, giving the coach suggestions on what days to practice hard and when to lighten up a bit. On Monday morning, touch base with the coaches so we can go over the reports.

- Monday to Thursday – College hockey has most of its games on the weekend. Therefore, these days of the week are pretty much the same in what we do with our players. Starting at 9:00 AM:

  - Players report to the weight room and weigh in.

  - They perform heart rate variability test. Their subjective questionnaires are reviewed.

  - Drop Jump – times and heights recorded.

  - 30–40 minutes of lifting, depending on the day.

  - Practice Time – 35–75 minutes depending on the day.

  - Record heart rate during practice.

  - Recovery work.

Because of the many games in professional hockey, Justin's weeks during the season will vary depending on how many games are being played. The athletes go through a more physical stretch when there are three to four games in a week, and the workouts need to be programmed so that some weeks have a high load while others are low.

Because of the erratic training schedule during the season, Justin performs constant testing on his players. He wants to make sure that each player is doing the right type of workout and the correct amount of work. If there is an area where a player might be weakening instead of getting stronger, then Justin institutes necessary changes to that player's routine. This is all a process, and you need to be willing to see things you do not like and be able to make changes.

This is the beauty of analytics in a nutshell. It allows you to track the progress — or lack of it — in every player. When you see something off-kilter, you can take steps to rectify the issue. Monitoring and analytics are often about identifying red flags before a major problem arises. The idea is to be able to head off any trouble, and make small, one percent changes. As we will talk about in the next chapter, often a strength coach and a sports coach have to get together because you need to modify what a player does in practice as well as the weight room to get the best results.

Let's assume you now know what equipment and tests you are going to use with your team. You have established your training schedule so that your players can improve speed, strength, and power. Everybody has bought into what you want to do. The next question is how do you organize all those numbers?

See Appendix Image on Page 151

There are different software programs available that allow you to accumulate data and organize it in any way that works for you. These are often known as Athlete Management Systems (AMS). They are a ready-made framework that can collect and analyze your data. The downside is that they can be somewhat restrictive and inflexible. For an expert in this area, they may not allow for advanced levels of detailed analytics. But for the novice and intermediate level program or coach, they can provide a valuable structure and simplify the analytics process.

Some equipment comes with its own software that can immediately download the results into a spreadsheet on a laptop, phone, or tablet. We mentioned that for things like having your players answering their subjective questions in the morning like "How do you feel?" or "How much sleep did you get?" that they can do on their phones. One thing about technology is that it does become cheaper as time goes on. It is worth your time to pay attention to websites and publications that talk about new equipment and techniques. It is possible to find new technology that allows you to do something cheaper and more efficiently than you are now.

In general, you want a chart or spreadsheet for each of your players. Just taking what we talked about throughout this book, you should have these categories:

- External Loading

- Internal Loading

- Jump and Power Profiling

- Anthropometrics

- Subjective Wellness and Workload Data

You can break these down into segments that reflect the data you gather on your players. By having a format that makes it easy to add more categories or subsections later, you will be prepared for any new testing techniques you might include in the future.

Whether some of the fields are automatically populated from a piece of equipment, or you manually input them, you want to be able to see at any moment how a particular athlete is doing. It should be in an easy-to-read format for trainers, coaches, and players. Just as you plot out your workout schedule, think about what you want your data chart to show. The more thought that goes into this ahead of time, the easier it will be to construct and implement your spreadsheet and system.

Often, this process of instantly visualizing and organizing data is referred to as a "dashboard." Whether you build your own programs using Excel or Google Docs, or you utilize an AMS, the athlete dashboards are just like the ones in your car. They allow you to quickly and efficiently see and understand your information. You are taking your data from simply a collection of numbers to a more nuanced picture of each of your athletes at any given time.

You want to build or improve on an analytical system for your team. The hardest situation to walk into is when you are the one taking the first steps to implement physiological analytics into your training program. Change is usually considered with suspicion. Do not be afraid to go out of your way to educate players, coaches, and other strength coaches on what you want to do and why.

Education is the key to success. You need to understand and be able to convey "why" you are doing what you are doing. When you can easily explain that to your players and coaches, and relate how it corresponds to their ultimate goals, then you begin to create buy-in and trust in the process.

Remember that the key to any group of people to have success as a team is for everyone to be on the same page. At times, it takes a little effort to get there. We know from experience that once your players and coaches associate their success with what you are trying to accomplish in the training room, they will wonder why it took so long to implement your concepts in the first place!

As you use the data to customize your players' training sessions and they see positive results in their various performance data, you will find them working harder as they buy into the process and understand the intent. When we first outfitted hockey players with heart monitors, many weren't very keen on it. However, it wasn't long before they would badger the strength coaches after practice or between periods of a game to see what their workload information was, such as calorie expenditure and recovery rate. The players had come to understand the correlation between their heart rate and performance. Now they had a more in-depth understanding why they needed to do extra conditioning work after practice, or some other type of training, because they understood their own data.

When you reach that point in your program, you will find that your players accept the analytics as much as they accept running around the field or weightlifting. As with most things in life, when people understand why they are doing something and, even more importantly, see positive results, they are going to take to any training like a fish to water.

Numbers are not everything. Analytics is not going to score the goal or throw the touchdown. However, by using those numbers to help a player become stronger and faster, it is going to give him an extra edge in performing his sport well. When we coach or train players, we all want as many tools in our toolbox as possible to help make our athletes and team better. Analytics is a very important tool you can continually refine to serve your team better. We all know that extra tenth of a second in speed or an extra inch in jumping ability could be the difference in executing some tremendous athletic play that can make a difference in a game.

See Appendix Images on Pages 150 through 153

FORCE PLATE		WATT BIKE		WEIGHT		BODY COMP		WEEKLY LOAD	
BASELINE	Current Week	BASELINE	Current Week	Ideal Weight	Current Weight	Prior Pinch	Current Pinch	Week Prior	Current Week
0	0.0	0.0	0	179	195.0	4.5		0	270
27.95	28.0	1063.0	1189	180	179.0	5.5	6.8	197	163
26.7	26.7	1316.0	1448	198	197.0	4.4	5.5	627	211
28.35	28.4	1501.0	1478	195	194.0	6.5	7.0	487	274
22.44	22.4	1222.0	0	212	215.0	10.4	10.2	0	307
28.7	28.7	1130.0	1354	200	197.0	8.8	9.5	298	208
22.44	22.4	1212.0	1338	213	208.0	10.3	10.2	109	207
28.35	28.4	1164.0	1223	202	202.7	8.1	8.5	686	358
29.13	29.1	1010.0	1425	208	205.0	8.2	8.0	345	376
25.2	25.2	1058.0	1341	206	207.0	8.2	9.3	347	184
28.7	28.7	1616.0	0	213	212.0	8.2	7.9	302	0
24.8	24.8	1390.0	1338	205	206.0	8.8	9.3	410	314
25.98	26.0	1260.0	1312	208	206.0	10.6	10.2	0	490
30.71	30.7	1434.0	1517	220	215.0	5.5	6.2	800	208
					202.0			0	271
31.1	31.1	1426.0	1326	222	225.0	12.0	11.1	95	256
31.5	31.5	1270.0	0	215	216.0	4.1	5.4	264	191
0	0.0	0.0	1361	198	197.0	6.7	7.4	663	156
31.89	31.9	1399.0	1778	216	218.0	9.1	7.2	315	33
24.4	24.4	1213.0	1441	206	208.0	6.8	7.1	548	340
25.2	25.2	1248.0	1328	232	235.0	14.5	13.0	263	180
27.95	28.0	1190.0	1246	187	187.0	7.1	6.8	0	100
27.17	27.2	1370.0	0	204	0.0	-	0.0	0	0
23.62	23.6	1214.0	0	222	0.0	10.3	11.4	455	0
25.98	26.0	1178.0	1464	202	197.0	9.6	8.8	224	248
28.7	28.7	1452.0	0	225	226.0	9.8	0.0	0	274
24.02	24.0	850.0	989	180	175.0	7.3	8.1	0	383
24.41	24.4	1155.0	1231	188	0.0	10.6	10.7	458	0

*We gather and track data weekly and are able to compare
so that we always know where our players are at and
how to change the stress we place them under.*

HI-MOD-LOW LOAD PROTOCOL

AVERAGE PRACTICE	15% PRACTICE TL	AVERAGE PRAC +15%	AVERAGE PRAC -15%	AVERAGE GAME	15% AVG GAME TL	AVERAGE GAME +15%	AVERAGE GAME -15%
165	24.75	189.75	140.25	563	84.45	647.45	478.55
187	28.05	215.05	158.95	447	67.05	514.05	379.95
118	17.7	135.7	100.3	429	64.35	493.35	364.65
132	19.8	151.8	112.2	332	49.8	381.8	282.2
183	27.45	210.45	155.55	471	70.65	541.65	400.35
192	28.8	220.8	163.2	305	45.75	350.75	259.25
136	20.4	156.4	115.6	282	42.3	324.3	239.7
112	16.8	128.8	95.2	452	67.8	519.8	384.2
116	17.4	133.4	98.6	306	45.9	351.9	260.1
99	14.85	113.85	84.15	359	53.85	412.85	305.15
101	15.15	116.15	85.85	341	51.15	392.15	289.85
	0	0	0		0	0	0
	0	0	0		0	0	0
	0	0	0		0	0	0
133	19.95	152.95	113.05	402	60.3	462.3	341.7
98	14.7	112.7	83.3	212	31.8	243.8	180.2
131	19.65	150.65	111.35	249	37.35	286.35	211.65
142	21.3	163.3	120.7	319	47.85	366.85	271.15
118	17.7	135.7	100.3	358	53.7	411.7	304.3
136	20.4	156.4	115.6	259	38.85	297.85	220.15
138	20.7	158.7	117.3	374	56.1	430.1	317.9
140	21	161	119	419	62.85	481.85	356.15
155	23.25	178.25	131.75	374	56.1	430.1	317.9
129	19.35	148.35	109.65	306	45.9	351.9	260.1
135	20.25	155.25	114.75	387	58.05	445.05	328.95
108	16.2	124.2	91.8	321	48.15	369.15	272.85
89	13.35	102.35	75.65	362	54.3	416.3	307.7
167	25.05	192.05	141.95	295	44.25	339.25	250.75
85	12.75	97.75	72.25	364	54.6	418.6	309.4
99	14.85	113.85	84.15	265	39.75	304.75	225.25
122	18.3	140.3	103.7	350	52.5	402.5	297.5
116	17.4	133.4	98.6	299	44.85	343.85	254.15
119	17.85	136.85	101.15	322	48.3	370.3	273.7
130.03	17.73	135.94	100.48	350.80	47.84	366.75	271.07
156.67	23.50	180.17	133.17	479.67	71.95	551.62	407.72
133.88	14.60	111.97	82.76	356.00	38.84	297.75	220.07
124.21	18.63	142.84	105.58	328.26	49.24	377.50	279.02

We can change the data on an individual basis based off high and low protocol.

SPORT SCIENCE REPORT

WEEK RECORD: 1-2

YEAR RECORD: 15-13-1

WEEK OF DEC 25-31, 2017

WEEKLY BRIEF

WORKLOAD—This week games Wednesday, Saturday and Sunday we had a high load. Coming off of the break loads were higher than normal being our first high intensity bout of activity after 3 days off. We came in at a good team average just below our goal of 1000. However some of our top guys were around 12-1400. Day off tomorrow will allow us to come into the week strong as we have another similar week coming up.

STRESS—Player stress loads were low through the week. The HRV scores were great on Thursday before leaving for the trip. The road trip has been pretty simple so minimizing player stress was good. The freshness and legs we showed in the 3rd game of the week in San Antonio and the 2nd in a day and a half was good to see. The gym visit on the travel day was a great play as is the yoga on Jan 1.

RECOVERY—Lower Recovery number this week. I would put that up to the 3 days off. In game recovery numbers not effected very much. From the one game we got.

OULIER---Goalies...they were evenly split with the players this week in terms of load...it showed in their play and loading I believe.

UPCOMING WEEK

WORKLOAD—We are going back into a week with 3 games and a back to back with a long travel day. We have a weekly training load goal of 1150, which we know approx. 900-1000 will go into games. With practice day Tuesday we will look to hit about 150 TL.

STRESS—I will be running some HRV numbers to see where the guys are falling on the trip as well as first day back. The travel schedule is very easy and should have little effect. The yoga on Jan 1 after NYE is a great idea and should aid in the body stress recovery.

RECOVERY—With 3 games in 4 days, sleep, nutrition and hydration becomes crucial. We are also dealing with a time change coming back from Texas, although gaining time is advantageous. The home games definitely help the situation, taking advantage of home ice and recovery is big over the next two weeks.

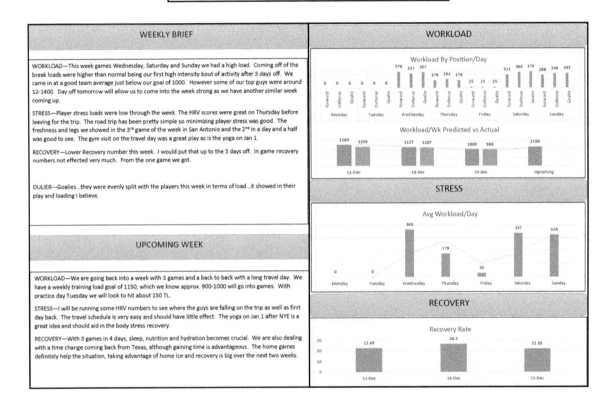

This is an example of a weekly sport science report given to coaches explaining our last week and what we need to do for our upcoming week.

9

Talking Coach

I f you are a coach with younger players, such as at the high school level, you might be the head coach, strength coach, transportation coordinator — you are a "Jack of all trades." You can make great use of the different practices we talk about in this book, though it might be on a very basic level. That is okay. It is certainly going to help you with the development of your players. We hope you see the merits of all we discussed here.

Larger programs have the benefit of assistant coaches, strength coaches, nutritionists, and any other person that you can afford to help with your program. Whatever the size of the program or sport, coaches are in charge of the team. As we said about athletes, no two coaches are going to be alike. You are going to have veterans and rookies. Some coaches played the sport they coach while others did not, but they immerse themselves in it so much that they know the sport inside and out. Some have embraced analytics for a long time, and others view it with a bit of skepticism.

Coaches have a tough job. When all is said and done, they are judged on wins and losses. Perhaps no other occupation in America or anywhere is judged with such black and white criteria. A coach epitomizes the "buck stops here" management philosophy. This is always an important fact to remember, especially as a support staff member. Head coaches do what they believe to be the best course of action for the team to win. This is often what is at the root of the "this is how we've always done it" mentality. After all, one does not become an experienced coach without having a fair amount of success! It is only natural to lean on what has helped create success in the past. As a strength coach considering implementing performance science practices, it is always important to keep these facts in mind.

In this chapter, we want to address coaches who are exploring the aspect of sport science we present in this book and to strength coaches who work with coaches. As strength coaches, we know it is invaluable to work with the coaching staff. Strength coaches, coaches, and players are a team within the team. We cannot work in a vacuum apart from the coaches in getting the athletes ready to play.

For a team not using the analytics we have been talking about so far, there is a lot of questioning about putting a numerical value on different aspects of a player's physical abilities. You need to be patient in explaining how this all works. When you talk to your coaches about what you are doing, you need to put it in terms they understand — namely, how this is going to help them win. This is what we call "speaking coach." You need to explain what you do and how you test players in a manner that is understandable to the head coach and the rest of the coaching staff.

We chose our profession because we love it. Head coaches might not love the weight room; thus we need to give them the opportunity to see the crossover and parallels of how we can help them and the team succeed. Coaches at every level are there to give the team the best opportunity to win. We try to show them how not to lose the game before the team steps on the field of battle.

As we talked about in an earlier chapter, numbers have been part of sports since they were invented. For generations, this mainly centered on what happened in a game. Shots on goal, batting average, yards per completion, percentage of three-point shots, and on and on. These are understandable and part of the game. It is always amazing during a broadcast of a World Series game when you hear something like, "That hasn't been done in a game since the 1921 Yankees." It boggles the mind how all those stats were kept throughout the decades.

Moneyball: The Art of Winning an Unfair Game by Michael Lewis is a book extolling the efforts of Oakland Athletics' general manager Billy Beane. He chose his players using an analytical, evidence-based, saber-metric approach. His approach to assembling talent expanded to many other teams in other sports. There was great value in studying the on-field analytics of players to determine if they would fit on a team. In the same way, the analytics you gather on your players' health and physiology can be a great help to a coach as to who should play in a game and how best to use them.

The performance analytics we track help us prepare our players to be successful. In our sport, we do not work with a player on how to improve shooting the puck at the net. It is not our role to improve sport-specific skills such as shooting and passing. That is the coach's job. Rather, we are tasked with developing the general and underlying qualities of athleticism: power, strength, speed, quickness. The development of these qualities is like the foundation to a pyramid — the wider and broader that foundation, the higher the skill development can be. Performance analytics allows us to understand better who our athletes are, what their foundation looks like, and where we can best make improvements.

See Appendix Image on Page 154

You want to use examples like this when you talk to a coach about what you are doing and how it is helping the team. If you can illustrate there is a correlation in the player's power analytics and his game contributions, you are going to have a coach believing in what you do. It is important to use words and phrases that sports coaches understand. It helps with the coach's buy-in.

Let's use another sport for a good example — football. A pro team had a great defensive lineman. He went all out on every play. The problem with this is that he burned out quickly and could only be used intermediately. Working with the team strength coaches, this player increased his power, speed, and endurance in the workouts that they put him through. Soon he went from being in for a third of the plays to at least half. The strength coaches did nothing regarding working on his football skills. They simply concentrated on the player's workouts to improve his physiology. By utilizing performance analytics, the strength coaches were able to pinpoint the appropriate type of conditioning work that the player needed and thus were able to broaden his foundation. This created trust with the head coach and trust leads to buy-in. The head coach came to trust his strength and conditioning staff to work on the raw athlete to make him better for skill development in his particular sport.

As we talked about in the analytics chapter, you accumulate a great deal of information. Another example showing how to use your data is from our experience of showing a coach how long a player should be on the ice. Hockey is a very fast sport where a player gives his all in very short bursts on the ice. A player's shift might be only 30 seconds to a minute. When you are studying players in a game situation where you can have them hooked up to an HR monitor and accelerometer, you can make certain judgments. Let's say Joe is an excellent player. When he is on the ice, the team does quite well in scoring goals and preventing goals from being scored. You keep track and see that his average ice time on a shift is 55 seconds. Further analysis shows that both the scoring average and goals-against average when he is out there deteriorates at the 47-second mark. Joe's quality of play goes down in that final eight seconds, and you see his body is laboring at that point based on heart rate.

Now you might think, "Eight seconds? Big deal!"

If most games are a matter of inches and seconds, it is a big deal. This type of information becomes invaluable to a coach in changing lines in a hockey game. Stressing shift lengths to players as a point of emphasis becomes imperative for continued success. It could ultimately be the difference between performing an error and having a goal scored against the team, or making a play and scoring a goal. If you demonstrate to a coach that keeping a certain player on the ice for too long has a rate of diminishing return, then he is going to adjust the timing of his lines accordingly. If Joe is his best player and the coach needs him at his peak, he is going to make sure he is out there at his optimum level. It is all about winning and losing.

One of the best ways a strength coach can help is by assisting in the organization of the week. The head coach will ultimately have the final say, but being able to get an idea as to how the week should be arranged from a physiological perspective will help the coach make informed decisions. The strength coach can help his coach by offering suggestions on how long a practice should be and at what pace. The coach decides what happens at practice, of course, but a strength coach is keeping track of the total workload a player is accumulating in his training as well as at practice and in games. Working out an athlete is as much a matter of adjusting his workload as the type of exercises he does. The body needs to recover from physical stress. It is an integral component of the body becoming stronger and quicker. Heavy and light workdays need to be alternated for an athlete's body to develop properly. It certainly does not help if you plan a light workout for the day, only to have the coach run the player around on the field until he is puking his guts out. That type of practice not only makes a player unhappy, but also ruins the idea of a required light load day.

Of course, this might be the correct course of action in the head coach's mind, but from a physiological perspective, it probably is not very helpful. "Speaking coach" is about relaying your concerns, while appreciating and understanding that there may be a more important reason for the coach to run his practice a certain way on a given day. Admitting this to a coach might go a long way to building a trusting relationship.

As mentioned in the previous chapter, Justin works with professional hockey players. They can go all out during a game three to four times a week, and he needs to adjust their daily workouts accordingly to keep the players as fresh as possible. The best way he can work with coaches on this problem is to show them, by the numbers, how players perform in a game in relation to their workouts. The key here is all about recovery. The stress a player undergoes in any game varies by the type of game it is. It could be physical or more free-flowing. He might spend lots of time on special teams, or it might be more five on five. Ice time comes into play too. One player might be fresher on his shifts for the entire game if the day prior was a light workout. Another player might be better if he has a rest day after a game and a moderate workout the day before he plays.

It depends on the player's total workload leading up to the day of the game. Some players respond to high CNS work prior to games while others do not. This is where the individual focus on player tracking and monitoring comes in. To use one metric, Justin might utilize the HRV in association with the loading of the day and week. He also knows that he can use the team's power tracking jump data as a chronic workload assessment of power.

Like a baseball player's batting average, the numbers you use are going to have more impact over an entire season. You can show how your players trend over a year and back it up with numbers. Another real-life example is how a college hockey team was able to increase their winning percentage when the training staff and the coaching staff were in sync. Daily workouts and practices were structured to do the proper amount of hard and easy workouts in an optimal sequence. The team thrived. The metrics of the athletes aided in establishing the structure. Constant testing helped back up what the team needed to do. As long as the team kept to the philosophy they set, there were more wins than losses.

As human beings, we seem to have this consistent failing of sticking to something that works. It might be because of boredom, trying a new idea, or laziness. Whatever the reason, we tend to get away from something that works for us. This is true across all walks of life, not just sports. Another advantage of keeping up with the analytics of your players is that you have something to look back on when things go sour. It is not uncommon for coaches to realize that they have to go back to what made them successful at some part of the season if they go into a slump. When you have the different metrics charted for the players, you have solid information to review to determine what you need to repeat doing.

Coaches are still going to rely on their experience and gut to some extent — all good coaches have that ability — but they are also thankful when they have good data to fall back on to figure things out and get the ship straightened out. This is why the sports coach and strength coach relationship is so important — to keep from jumping ship when things are bad, and to keep to the routine and not get lazy when things are good.

When you work with a coach, you have to gain his trust. You cannot come in and say your ideas are the best thing since the invention of the universal gym. One thing coaches have in common is that they would rather see a sermon than hear one. You have to back up your ideas with results. As the coaches see that what you are doing with players translates into steady incremental progress in each athlete, they are going to buy into more of what you are doing.

Here is one of the most important words in the English language, whether it is in sports, working on Wall Street, or in a relationship with your spouse or kids: communication. Testing your athletes and interpreting those results where a coach understands what you are doing and the value it provides is paramount. Once the coach comprehends and buys into what you are doing, then you have to keep up the dialogue throughout the season. Just as a baseball manager needs to trust his pitching coach, you want your coach to embrace what you provide for the players.

A lesson about going in for a job interview is that you want to convince the person interviewing you that you can help solve his problem. It does not matter what kind of job it is; the fact is that we are all hired to provide solutions. As a coach, you must figure out how to win. If you are a strength coach, you need to help develop athletes with winning characteristics and aid the coach in figuring out how to win. If what you do with the players in the off-season, training camp, and during the season does that, then you are doing your job.

Another workplace employment tip is to document what you are doing. When it comes time for reviews, you want to show your superiors your accomplishments. In sports, we do not have the luxury of an annual or even a quarterly review. They happen after each and every game. All you have to do is look at how a coach is fired after a particularly bad loss, or an assistant coach is let go in the same circumstances. It can happen to strength coaches too. At the end of the 2017 baseball season, the training staff of the New York Mets was released because their pitching staff was on injured reserve more than they were playing.

If you are recording and using your data, you are documenting what you are doing every day. Even more importantly, it shows how each player is improving and adding value to the team. All the tests and metrics in the world are not going to help the team unless you show the coach how to use those numbers to put the athletes in the best possible position to win.

Justin is explaining what is going on with heart rate and accelerometer data during a drill practice. Following page: This shows the comparison of the training camp numbers to mid-season. They get weekly reports but over a long period of time they are able to buy into the improvements and change — especially when it is reflected in the results in games.

Power Tracking

FORCE PLATE		WATT BIKE		WEIGHT		BODY COMP	
Trainging Camp	Dec-17	Training Camp	Dec-17	Training Camp	Dec-17	Training Camp	Dec-17
25.2	25.2	1058.0	1341	209	208.0	8.9	9.2
26.36	27.2	1482.0	1361	197	196.5	6.5	5.7
28	28.0	1063.0	1189	180	180.0	6.3	5.1
27.2	-	1370.0	-	205	-	6.9	-
22.4	22.4	1222.0	1355	215	214.0	10.4	9.2
28.7	28.7	1482.0	1452	225	226.0	10.5	9.8
31.1	31.1	1426.0	1326	222	224.0	10.2	9.4
29.1	29.1	1010.0	1425	212	203.0	7.6	7.0
-	-	-	-	-	193.0	-	7.7
31.9	31.9	1399.0	1778	214	218.0	12.6	11.3
28	28.0	1190.0	1246	187	186.0	6.4	6.2
-	-	-	-	218	210.0	10.3	8.7
28.7	28.7	1616.0	1679	212	213.5	8.1	7.7
31.5	31.5	1270.0	1322	213	214.5	4.6	4.7
24	24.0	850.0	989	177	177.0	7.9	8.1
28.4	28.4	1501.0	1478	193	193.4	7.4	6.3
22.4	22.4	1212.0	1338	210	208.0	9.8	8.2
26	26.0	1178.0	1464	202	199.8	8.4	7.9
25.2	25.2	1248.0	1328	236	235.0	13.5	14.5
26.2	26.2	1343.0	1376	169	173.3	6.1	6.0
24.4	24.4	1213.0	1441	208	205.1	7.0	6.9
24.8	24.8	1390.0	1338	205	209.0	8.6	8.2
26.7	26.7	1316.0	1448	198	198.0	5.6	5.5
28.7	28.7	1130.0	1354	200	196.0	9.5	8.2

10

Talking Player

While you work with your players day in and day out to the point that you see them more than your family, do not assume that they are accepting everything you tell them just because it is coming out of your mouth. If you think you are under stress to win as a coach or strength coach, remember the players. They are the ones who have to fight for a position on the team, master the team's system, be mentally and physically prepared for every game, work their butts off between games, and be ready to do it again after every win or loss.

Players are conditioned to do what the coaches and strength coaches want, at least when they are young and inexperienced. They quickly realize that everything they are asked to do in practice or during workouts might not make a lot of sense. However, if they understand why they are doing something and they see a benefit to it, they are going to accept it and give the effort required to see physiological and mechanical gains necessary to continue to develop and expand their careers. When they see positive results from something, they are going to jump on it, no matter what that "something" is.

As with coaches, your job as a strength coach is to effectively communicate with your players what you are doing with the various equipment and accumulated data, and why. Of course, the intention of what you want to do is to help the athlete develop and become better. A player should automatically buy into that premise, but it might take a lot more explaining why increased success in a jump test leads to better performance on the field, court, or ice. It is always important to remember as a strength coach that your athletes are on the team to play their sport, not to train in the weight room. Educating them on the "why" behind what you do is crucial to creating buy-in. Be approachable and let them know you will give them whatever they need or ask for. Also, let them know that you are not gathering data or measuring them constantly to work against them.

It also helps to go back to what we said in the analytics chapter about being thoroughly knowledgeable of any equipment or test you put the athletes through. It's human nature to have more confidence in someone who knows what he is doing. You want to demonstrate to your players that they can trust in what you want them to do.

We want to talk about an important concept related to knowing what you are doing. Yes, you want to show that you know your job. However, that does not mean when you are hit with a question where you do not know the answer that you make one up. It might give the impression at the time that you know your stuff, but it will not take long before someone proves you wrong. Nothing ruins trust more than giving inaccurate information. There is absolutely nothing wrong with saying, "I don't know the answer to that, but I will find out for you." If you find that answer as quickly as you can, you are building up that trust. The players realize they can go to you with their questions and concerns, and you will give them a straight answer. That is a quality people appreciate no matter what profession they work in.

As with explaining analytics to coaches, the best way to win players over is to show them how the results of their training lead to good results for them as a player. By bringing the entire team into the process, you can have results you did not expect that enforces what you are doing to the players. As an example that had two different positive results, we want to share with you what happened with the 10-yard sprint.

You can easily do this test with your players in any sport. It is simply a 10-yard sprint that you can run in a weight room or any indoor space to help promote quickness and explosiveness in your players. The players are supposed to run at their maximum speed. Since we are hockey strength coaches, our real-life examples are related to our players. Players run the test every week, and the strength coaches record, rank, and broadcast the results, so the team knows what every player did. We have stated a few times in this book that promoting competition within the team during workouts is a good way to keep it fresh and garner enthusiasm.

The first player we want to talk about was fast. In fact, most weeks he was the one with the quickest time. However, this speed did not translate on the ice. In practice, other players that he smoked in the 10-yard sprint constantly beat him. Bringing this discrepancy in his sprint times and his skating speed to the attention of the coaches, they realized that his skating technique was off. If they did not have the data from the sprint and only watched him on the ice, they might not have realized he had such raw speed. By working more with the skating coach, the player was able to transfer his off-ice power and speed onto the ice.

This example shows you two key things. As we illustrated in the last chapter, whenever you show data to a coach and relate how that can translate into helping improve a player and the team, you are providing a valuable service. When you show the player what you figured out by analyzing data and relate how that information is going to help them as a player, they are going to be more enthusiastic about being tested and analyzed for anything you want. Here is a perfect case of cementing what you are doing with both the coaching staff and the players. After all, players talk, and if you help one, she is going to be singing your praises to everyone. The key is being able to relate the information in a way that they can understand, and show how it is useful to them and their specific goals.

A common question to running the 10-yard sprint or any other test where the team sees everyone's result is how do the slower players react. Do they get discouraged? It is possible, but one of the roles of the strength coach conducting the test is to keep up the team's enthusiasm for the different activities. This is where you want to engage all the players.

A great example of the balance between motivation and embarrassment is illustrated with this true story. There was an athlete who was notoriously slow in the 10-yard sprint. You could time him with a calendar. With the results posted every week, everyone could see that he was last among the group. The player contended with his slow pace like you hope any athlete would. He tried to get better. In the beginning, he wasn't beating anyone, so he just competed with himself.

The strength coach stepped in and worked with the athlete using a proactive approach. The coach took the player aside and used this as a teaching movement, relating what they were doing in training for speed development. He provided a few important technique cues to the athlete, so he could better understand the nuances of training and how it carried over to speed and acceleration. The athlete saw an opportunity to improve his game and was willing to listen and absorb the lessons because it related to him and his goals. As he cut down his time, the player's confidence grew. His teammates encouraged him. If something like a simple 10-yard race could help bring a team together, it did so this time. When the player finally beat one of his teammates, you would have thought he won the Stanley Cup. So did the rest of the team!

When you can help an athlete get better, as well as engage him and all the team in what you are doing with their workouts, your job is going to be easier and more enjoyable. It is all about setting a culture. When you win over the players, the next group is going to learn from the veterans that what you do is valuable.

As these tools and techniques continue to provide value to the individual and the team, and as a trust from that educational process grows, buy-in becomes the norm. Before you realize it, one season grows into two, and every class or group of players who absorb the culture come to expect the sport science applications being part of their training. They become the standard, and they are accepted as valuable and crucial to the team culture.

A situation that illustrates this was when we started hooking up players with heart rate monitors. As with anything new, it was treated with skepticism. When the players understood what it was all about and how their heart rate was a good way to gauge how they were doing, they were lining up to see their results. This helped when new players came through the door the following year. The veterans were fully engaged in the program, and the newcomers simply followed their example. You know your system is working when your older players provide that type of leadership and support for your program.

This brings up another common question. How do veteran players react to the different concepts and testing we share in this book? Even more so than the new arrivals on the team, you have to show the veterans the results. A great case in point is a veteran NHL player who came onto a team that measured different analytics. This player was set in his training routine because it worked for him so well over time. However, he started to slow down a little on the ice. The strength coaches recorded the power tracking of all the players, and they were able to show the player that his power was on a downward track. The coaches were able to correlate the player's concern of "not feeling it" to an actual decrease in anaerobic power production and peak power. By offering a few suggestions to change up his weekly routine and the volume of work he was performing in a given week, the player began to improve his power and this, in turn, ramped up his game. He certainly began to see the value of the tracking and the analytics.

Another example from the pro game concerns a goaltender. Being a goaltender is a unique position in itself. They are often very set in a routine and do not like change. In this case, the goalie was a high draft pick, practiced well, but when it was game time, he felt exhausted. The coaches did not understand it because he would say he felt fine before a game, but soon his legs felt heavy, and coaches would see that he was tired. His rebound control was not there, he seemed to react slowly to shots, and his statistics did not reflect his talent level; in other words, he was underperforming. They would watch his practice throughout the week and could not understand how he became fatigued halfway through the game or was not as sharp as he should have been. For a position that relies on quickness, this is not what you want to see from your goalie. His goals against average was going up and save percentage was going down. The talent was there; the production was not.

By analyzing his workouts and practice, the strength coach saw that he was carrying a high load in workouts and practices. In fact, the practices tended to be high intensity. The goalie's heart rate curves were similar to that of a forward. This was causing a load almost double any other player on the ice. This was a case where the cliché, "Don't leave your game on the practice field," was true. The strength coach spoke to the head coach and showed him the numbers so that he was able to understand exactly what was going on. A simple change in the order of drills is all the fix that was needed for the intensity and training loads to balance correctly.

Whenever you can pinpoint the problem a player is having, you are enhancing everyone's buy-in to the program. One more hockey example is how a team juggled their lines. As we said before, hockey players are out there for very short, intense shifts. One team was relying too much on their first two lines. This meant that six forwards had consistently high loads very early in the game. These players were out there for their regular shifts, plus going out to kill penalties and being on the power plays. What you were having was a few of your top players cramping up and being noticeably less effective as the game went into the second and third periods.

The strength coach looked at the various data on the players and working with the coaches, the third and fourth lines received more ice time. This gave the first two lines more rest, and they became much more effective when they did go out on the ice. The strength coach was able to inform the coach of what was going on by giving him numerical evidence to what he knew to be true with what he saw. This empowered the head coach to be creative and find the solution within his talent as a coach. The two top lines became more productive throughout the game.

Again, the strength coaches proved invaluable to the coaches, and the players were happy. Players that need rest received it during the game, and other players got to play more. The top six forwards and top four defensemen were able to be more productive, and the other members of the team were given the opportunity to contribute. Using analytics is great when it helps make informed decisions. It also helps prove to the players that so much data is collected to have an impact on the day-to-day decisions and planning of a season. This further cements in their minds why it is so important.

There are many examples of physiological analytics used in other sports. Basketball looks at how many minutes a player is most effective in a game. Pitch count has become important in baseball. When trainers monitor the strength of a pitcher's arm, they can work with the coaching staff to determine the maximum number of pitches the player can throw before losing effectiveness. As we saw in football, some players have to be regulated to only a certain number of plays per game.

Whatever your sport, by knowing your players through personal interaction and monitoring the results of the different tests you conduct, you are going to help the players become better. In turn, you become an asset for helping the coach utilize those players. As you can see, though, to be effective in your job, you cannot be satisfied with only recording and charting numbers. You need to be able to take those results and communicate what they mean to your coaches and players. You also have to know how to improve or tweak workouts so that you can help players develop and improve.

One thing in sports has always been clear — you need to win. Another fact is that knowledge is power. Good teams scout opponents and great coaches know how to exploit any weaknesses in the team they are competing against. We are still in the early stage of understanding how much we know about our own athletes is going to pay dividends in the "win" column. A coach knows a player's talent, but this component of improving that player's physiology to get the most out of his talent has not been around long. The team, the coach, the athlete, and the strength coach who understands the significance of all we talk about in this book is going to have a firm edge over the competition that does not.

Justin is explaining info off of the Wattbike 6 sec sprint.

Conclusion

It is now up to you to start formulating what you want to do with your players based on the information you have here. Do not work in a vacuum. Set up a tentative plan and talk with your coaches. Remember, the things you do are ultimately going to require buy-in from the coaches and the players. The more you understand what you want to do, how you want to do it, and what it will show, the easier this will become part of the team routine.

The world of sport science is constantly changing. We are constantly learning new concepts and actively taking part in conferences, reading new materials, and doing research on the internet. It is like our work with athletes. We might work with them to help realize a one percent gain in their power numbers. In a game, that might make all the difference. If we discover a way to improve one of our tests or drills just a smidge, that might be enough to help that athlete grow that one percent.

A journey of a thousand miles begins with a single step. We have given you a great deal of practical information. Take it and help your players and your team. We will continue to provide new resources to assist our fellow strength coaches.

Let us know how you are doing!

Appendix

This represents information from page 18-19

Breaking down internal load by position and by day can paint a picture of the individual differences inherent within the team setting.

Physiologically based training load data can be tracked, quantified, and visualized to provide important information about on field workloads.

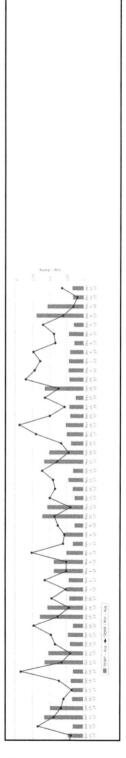

This represents information from page 22

This is how we track weekly loading parameters to ensure we are staying within our goal.

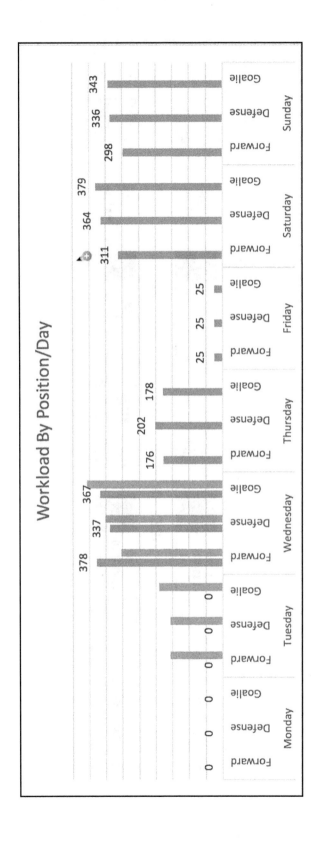

The images on page 138 through 140 represent information from page 22

These are gauges for where loads should be on a daily or weekly basis.

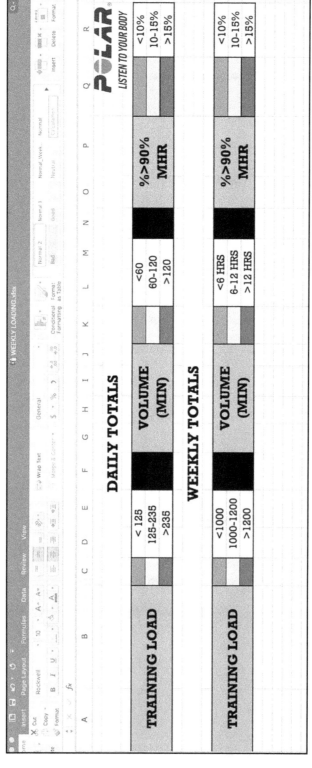

This is the daily morning HRV data that is viewed for each player. It provides immediate, weekly and long-term results that we use to determine the player's readiness and current training state.

COLUMNS ▾

Date ▲	Readiness Score (1-10)	ANS Balance (S/PS)	HRV Score (1-100)	7 day HRV CV
2018-01-12	9	S	62	15.3%
2018-01-11	10	PS	68	18.3%
2018-01-09	6	S	51	n/a
2018-01-08	Open Reading	n/a	74	n/a
2017-12-29	7	S	67	n/a
2017-12-27	9	S	64	9.3%
2017-12-20	8	PS	82	15.6%
2017-12-19	9	PS	71	14.2%
2017-12-18	7	PS	75	14.7%
2017-12-15	10	PS	65	11.7%
2017-12-14	8	S	53	14.3%
2017-12-12	8	PS	71	n/a
2017-12-11	8	PS	62	n/a
2017-12-02	5	S	62	9.8%
2017-11-30	6	PS	77	3.7%
2017-11-29	8	PS	76	n/a
2017-11-28	6	PS	72	n/a
2017-11-20	7	S	64	7.1%
2017-11-16	7	S	65	7.6%
2017-11-15	5	PS	74	n/a

The images on page 141 through 143 represent information from page 33

Timing gates provide reliable data on speed development.

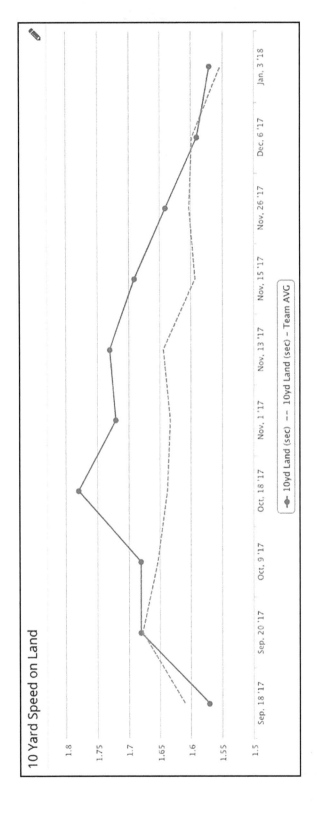

10 Yard Speed on Land

These two images identify asymmetries in power production between on and off ice expressions of power.

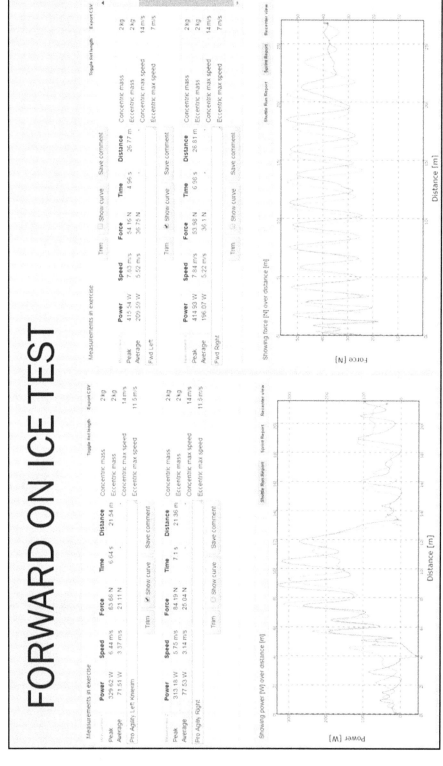

FORWARD ON ICE TEST

FORWARD OFF ICE TESTING CONT.
BLUE IS LEFT LAT BOUND; LEFT UNDER

Measurements in exercise

Toggle foot length | Export CSV

	Power	Speed	Force	Time	Distance		Concentric mass	2 kg
Peak	249.38 W	5.18 m/s	49.19 N	1.35 s	4.98 m		Eccentric mass	2 kg
Average	121.75 W	3.61 m/s	33.37 N				Concentric max speed	14 m/s
							Eccentric max speed	5.8 m/s

Xover Left under

Trim | ☑ Show curve | Save comment

	Power	Speed	Force	Time	Distance		Concentric mass	2 kg
Peak	261 W	5.39 m/s	48.64 N	1.42 s	5.01 m		Eccentric mass	2 kg
Average	118.32 W	3.4 m/s	34.26 N				Concentric max speed	14 m/s
							Eccentric max speed	5.8 m/s

Xover Right under

Trim | ☐ Show curve | Save comment

Showing speed [m/s] over distance [m]

Shuttle Run Report | Sprint Report | Recorder view

Speed [m/s] — Distance [m]

Measurements in exercise

Toggle foot length | Export CSV

	Power	Speed	Force	Time	Distance		Concentric mass	2 kg
Peak	178.04 W	3.93 m/s	46.42 N	2.25 s	4.99 m		Eccentric mass	2 kg
Average	81.93 W	2.2 m/s	27.14 N				Concentric max speed	14 m/s
							Eccentric max speed	5.8 m/s

Lat Bound Right

Trim | ☑ Show curve | Save comment

	Power	Speed	Force	Time	Distance		Concentric mass	2 kg
Peak	130.31 W	3.39 m/s	41.75 N	2.35 s	4.99 m		Eccentric mass	2 kg
Average	62.66 W	2.12 m/s	26.4 N				Concentric max speed	14 m/s
							Eccentric max speed	5.8 m/s

Lat Bound Left

Trim | ☐ Show curve | Save comment

	Power	Speed	Force	Time	Distance		Concentric mass	2 kg
Peak	146.22 W	3.74 m/s	43.13 N	2.01 s	4.99 m		Eccentric mass	2 kg

Showing speed [m/s] over distance [m]

Shuttle Run Report | Sprint Report | Recorder view

Speed [m/s] — Distance [m]

This represents information from page 60

This shows a squat jump using the 1080 Sprint and obtaining valuable power numbers to be compared over different weeks.

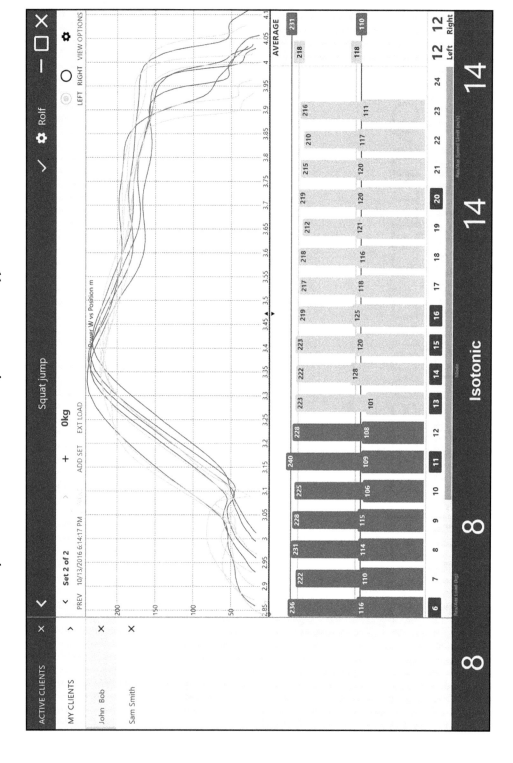

The images on this page through 149 represent information from page 63

These image shows the data off of the force plate for jump testing.

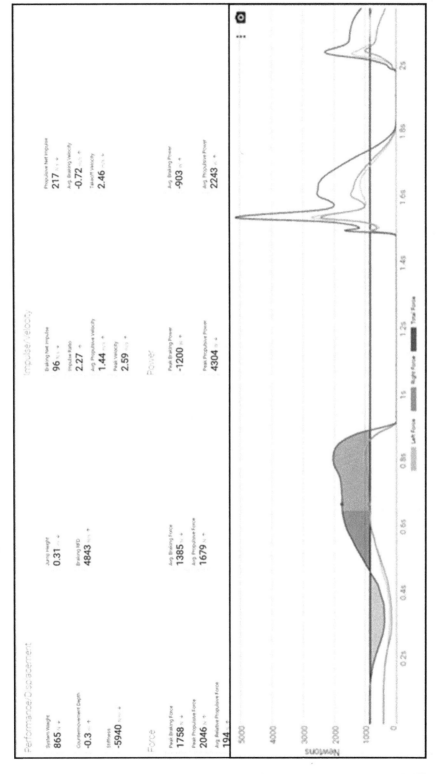

Performance Displacement

System Weight	865
Countermovement Depth	-0.3
Stiffness	-5940
Jump Height	0.31
Braking RFD	4843

Impulse Velocity

Braking Net Impulse	96
Impulse Ratio	2.27
Avg Propulsive Velocity	1.44
Peak Velocity	2.59
Propulsive Net Impulse	217
Avg Braking Velocity	-0.72
Takeoff Velocity	2.46

Force

Peak Braking Force	1758
Peak Propulsive Force	2046
Avg Relative Propulsive Force	194
Avg Braking Force	1385
Avg Propulsive Force	1679

Power

Peak Braking Power	-1200
Peak Propulsive Power	4304
Avg Braking Power	-903
Avg Propulsive Power	2243

Timing

Unweighting Phase	0.38
Braking Phase	0.18
Propulsive Phase	0.27
Flight Time	0.57
Unweighting Phase %	46
Braking Phase %	22
Propulsive Phase %	32

Symmetry

L/R Peak Braking Force	-1.25
L/R Peak Propulsive Force	3.13
L/R Avg Braking RFD	-10.94
L/R Propulsive Impulse Index	2.57
L/R Avg Braking Force	0.98
L/R Avg Propulsive Force	1.3
L/R Braking Impulse Index	1.92

Braking Force

Landing Performance

Force

Peak Braking Force
1758

Peak Propulsive Force
2046

Avg Relative Propulsive Force
194

Avg Braking Force
1385

Avg Propulsive Force
1679

Power

Peak Braking Power
-1200

Peak Propulsive Power
4304

Avg Braking Power
-903

Avg Propulsive Power
2243

Timing

Unweighting Phase
0.38

Braking Phase
0.18

Propulsive Phase
0.27

Flight Time
0.57

Unweighting Phase %
46

Braking Phase %
22

Propulsive Phase %
32

Asymmetry

L/R Peak Braking Force
-1.25

L/R Peak Propulsive Force
3.13

L/R Avg Braking RFD
-10.94

L/R Propulsive Impulse Index
2.57

L/R Avg Braking Force
0.98

L/R Avg Propulsive Force
1.3

L/R Braking Impulse Index
1.92

Landing Force

Peak Landing Force
5141

Relative Peak Landing Force
594

Avg Landing Force
1220

Landing Performance

Time to Stabilization
N/A

Stiffness
-1985

Landing Asymmetry

L/R Peak Landing Force
5.62

L/R Landing Impulse Index
N/A

L/R Avg Landing Force
2.55

These graphs show how we compare data from various vertical jump variations to gain better insight.

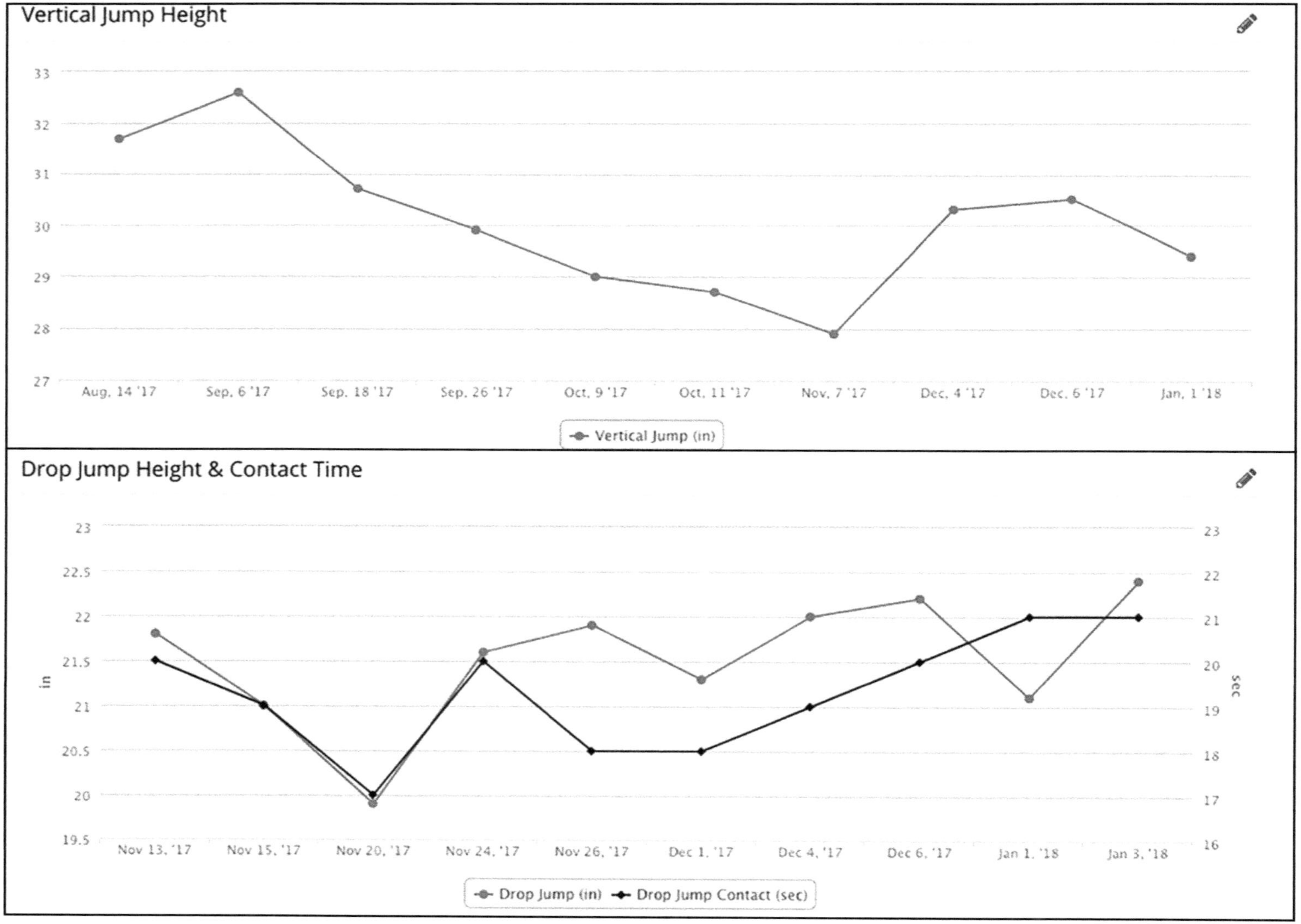

Vertical Jump Height

Y-axis: 33, 32, 31, 30, 29, 28, 27

X-axis: Aug. 14 '17, Sep. 6 '17, Sep. 18 '17, Sep. 26 '17, Oct. 9 '17, Oct. 11 '17, Nov. 7 '17, Dec. 4 '17, Dec. 6 '17, Jan. 1 '18

Legend: Vertical Jump (in)

Drop Jump Height & Contact Time

Left Y-axis (in): 23, 22.5, 22, 21.5, 21, 20.5, 20, 19.5

Right Y-axis (sec): 23, 22, 21, 20, 19, 18, 17, 16

X-axis: Nov. 13, '17, Nov. 15, '17, Nov. 20, '17, Nov. 24, '17, Nov. 26, '17, Dec 1, '17, Dec 4, '17, Dec 6, '17, Jan 1, '18, Jan 3, '18

Legend: Drop Jump (in), Drop Jump Contact (sec)

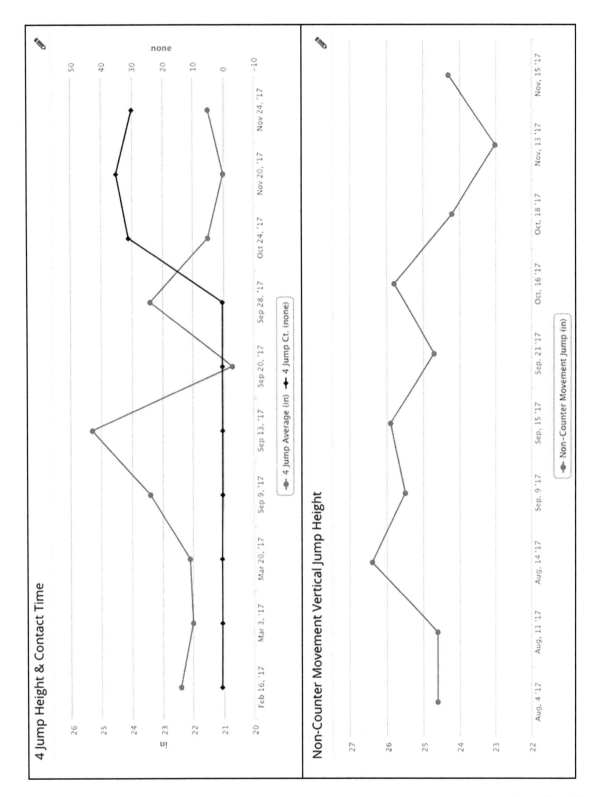

The images on this page through 153 represent information from page 110

We plan annually to make sure that we have a plan going into every week.

ANNUAL PLAN

Competition Week	Date (Monday)	Home	Away	Competitions	Competition	Weekly Training Load	Intensity	Volume	Unload Weeks
1	29-Sep	x		USA U-18/SIMON FRASER	EXHIB	1200	H	H	
2	6-Oct	x	x	BOWLING GREEN X2	NON CONF	1000	M	M	
3	13-Oct	x	x	OHIO STATE X2		1200	M	H	
4	20-Oct	x		ST LAWRENCE X2		1000	H	M	
5	27-Oct		x	MINNESOTA DULUTH X2		1300	M	M	
6	3-Nov	x		COLORADO COLLEGE X2	NCHC	1200	H	M	
7	10-Nov		x	NORTH DAKOTA X2		900	M	L	x
8	17-Nov	x		WESTERN MICHIGAN X2		1200	M	M	
9	24-Nov			OFF WEEK		1100	M	H	
10	1-Dec	x		NEBRASKA OMAHA X2		1200	H	M	
11	8 DEC			OFF WEEK		900	M	L	x
12	15-Dec			OFF WEEK		1200	H	H	
13	22-Dec		x	FLA HOCKEY CLASSIC 28/29	NON CONF	1200	M	H	
14	29-Dec		x	RPI X2		1000	H	M	
15	5-Jan		x	ST CLOUD X2		1200	M	H	
16	12-Jan			OFF WEEK		900	M	L	x
17	19-Jan	x		DENVER X2		1300	H	H	
18	26-Jan		x	WESTERN MICHIGAN X1		1200	M	H	
19	2-Feb			WESTERN MICHIGAN– OUTDOOR		900	M	L	x
20	9-Feb		x	COLORADO COLLEGE X2		1200	H	M	
21	16-Feb	x		MINNESOTA DULUTH X2		1300	M	M	
22	23-Feb		x	DENVER X2		900	H	L	x
23	2-Mar	x		NORTH DAKOTA X2		1200	H	M	
24	9-Mar	x		NCHC CONFERENCE TOURNEY	CONT TOURNEY	1100	H	M	
25	16-Mar		x	NCHC CONFERENCE CHAMPS		1000	M	M	
26	23-Mar		x	NCAA REGIONALS	NCAAS	1200	H	M	
27	30-Mar			OFF WEEK		900	M	L	x
28	6-Apr		x	Final Four		1000	L	M	

Tracking Acute:Chronic Workload fluctuations helps to quantify how much work is being done over the short and long term.

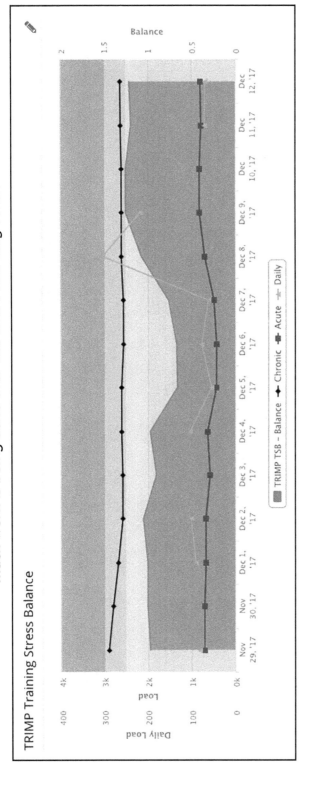

We can manipulate the weeks during the year and the annual plan.

WEEK OF: 1-Oct-12	DAY / DATE	MONDAY	TUESDAY	WEDNESDAY	THURSDAY	FRIDAY	SATURDAY	SUNDAY	WEEKLY TRAINING LOAD
Training / Competition		LIFT	LIFT	LIFT	REGEN	REGEN	GAME	GAME	
Training Phase					EARLY IN-SEASON				
TEAM % Game Intensity		60%	80%	100%	80%	100%	100%		
Game TL 225 Training Vol. (min)		120	120	120	100	140	140	0	12.3
Training Load #		125	225	176	180	245	245		1196
%>90%MHR		10%	12%	15%	12%	15%	15%	0%	
2.00 Daily Summary									
Intensity		LOW	HIGH	MOD	HIGH	HIGH	HIGH		
Volume		LOW	MOD	HIGH	LOW	HIGH	HIGH		

DAILY TOTALS

TRAINING LOAD	VOLUME (MIN)	%>90% MHR
<125	<60	<10%
125-215	60-120	10-15%
>215	>120	>15%

WEEKLY TOTALS

TRAINING LOAD	VOLUME (MIN)	%>90% MHR
<1000	<6 HRS	<10%
1000-1200	6-12 HRS	10-15%
>1200	>12 HRS	>15%

WEEK OF: 1-Oct-12	DAY / DATE	MONDAY	TUESDAY	WEDNESDAY	THURSDAY	FRIDAY	SATURDAY	SUNDAY	WEEKLY TRAINING LOAD
Training / Competition		LIFT	LIFT	LIFT	REGEN	GAME	GAME	OFF	
Training Phase					EARLY IN-SEASON				
TEAM % Game Intensity		60%	80%	100%	60%	100%	100%	0%	
Game TL 225 Training Vol. (min)		80	80	80	60	120	120	0	9.0
Training Load # 225		100	125	200	100	225	225	0	975
%>90%MHR		8%	12%	15%	8%	15%	15%	0%	
2.00 Daily Summary									
Intensity		LOW	MOD	HIGH	HIGH	HIGH	HIGH		
Volume		LOW	LOW	MOD	LOW	HIGH	HIGH		

YELLOW WEEK

WEEK OF:	DAY	MONDAY	TUESDAY	WEDNESDAY	THURSDAY	FRIDAY	SATURDAY	SUNDAY	WEEKLY TRAINING LOAD
1-Oct-12	DATE								
Training / Competition		LIFT	LIFT	LIFT	REGEN	REGEN	GAME	GAME	
Training Phase					EARLY IN-SEASON				
TEAM	% Game Intensity	60%	80%	100%	80%	100%	100%		10.0
225 Game TL	Training Vol. (min)	100	90	90	80	120	120	0	
	Training Load #	**100**	**150**	**200**	**115**	**225**	**225**		1015
%>90%MHR	%>90%MHR	8%	12%	15%	12%	15%	15%	0%	
2.00									
	Daily Summary								
	Intensity	LOW	MOD	HIGH	MOD	HIGH	HIGH		
	Volume	LOW	MOD	MOD	HIGH	HIGH	HIGH		

JANUARY ---- DAYS HOME: 23 DAYS ROAD: 12

MONTH TOTAL: 5620

DAILY PRACTICE FACTORS	MONDAY	TUESDAY	WEDNESDAY	THURSDAY	FRIDAY	SATURDAY	SUNDAY	WEEKLY TRAINING LOAD	
	1	2	3	4	5	6	7		DAYS HOME 3
Internal/External Load			GAME AT TEXAS	TRAVEL NO TL	GAME VS SAN JOSE	GAME VS SAN JOSE	OFF NO TL	1150	DAYS ROAD 4
Volume (time)/Distance Covered									
Intensity (%>90%MHR)/(%speed zone)									
Int+Ext Comb. Training Load									
	8	9	10	11	12	13	14		DAYS HOME 7
Internal/External Load			GAME VS SAN JOSE			GAME VS TUSCON	TRAVEL NO TL	1220	DAYS ROAD 0
Volume (time)/Distance Covered									
Intensity (%>90%MHR)/(%speed zone)									
Int+Ext Comb. Training Load									
	15	16	17	18	19	20	21		DAYS HOME 3
Internal/External Load	GAME AT TUSCON		GAME AT TUSCON	OFF NO TL	GAME VS SAN JOSE	GAME VS SAN JOSE		1350	DAYS ROAD 4
Volume (time)/Distance Covered									
Intensity (%>90%MHR)/(%speed zone)									
Int+Ext Comb. Training Load									
	22	23	24	25	26	27	28		DAYS HOME 3
Internal/External Load					GAME AT BAKERSFIELD	GAME AT BAKERSFIELD	OFF ALL STAR	1100	DAYS ROAD 4
Volume (time)/Distance Covered									
Intensity (%>90%MHR)/(%speed zone)									
Int+Ext Comb. Training Load									
	29	30	31	1	2	3	4		DAYS HOME 7
Internal/External Load	OFF ALL STAR	OFF ALL STAR				GAME VS TUSCON	OFF NO TL	800+	DAYS ROAD 0
Volume (time)/Distance Covered									
Intensity (%>90%MHR)/(%speed zone)									
Int+Ext Comb. Training Load									

This represents information from page 117

This relates the internal and external metrics to metrics that coaches care about and understand.

Start Date Time	Duration	% Time >85%HR Max	% Time 65-84% HR Max	% Time >65% HR Max	% Time < HR at AT	% Time > HR at AT	Peak HR	Average HR	Average HR Variability (SDNN)	Max HR Variability (SDNN)	Average HR Recovery	Max HR Recovery	Average Core Temp	Max Core Temp	Total Calories burned	Physiological Load	Physiological Intensity	Mechanical Load	Mechanical Intensity	Average Shift Time	shifts	time on ice	b/min	b/shift	Training Load
11/8/17 18:31	2:59:59	18.29	28.88	52.83	39.46	60.54	195	131.45	64.19	142.00	35.00	35.00	99.81	100.40	2319	433	3.32	199	2.66	0.60	32.00	19.27	16.40	9.87	315.94
11/8/17 18:30	3:00:39	34.49	34.54	30.97	45.51	54.49	189	135.99	62.29	117.00	45.00	45.00	100.15	101.30	2401	677	3.99	224	2.85	0.58	35.00	20.16	22.33	12.86	450.10
11/8/17 18:29	3:01:31	19.58	33.47	46.94	25.27	74.73	193	122.84	58.86	127.00	19.00	19.00	99.85	100.40	2231	472	3.37	133	2.68	0.57	29.00	16.51	18.32	10.43	302.38
11/8/17 18:29	3:01:19	20.60	45.25	34.16	51.82	48.18	207	140.24	56.11	144.00	44.00	44.00	100.23	101.30	2618	530	3.66	154	2.86	0.58	30.00	17.45	19.61	11.41	342.26
11/8/17 18:31	3:00:09	6.57	50.53	42.90	45.37	54.63	194	138.28	49.70	97.00	23.00	23.00	99.84	100.76	1928	733	4.42	184	3.25	0.69	30.00	20.56	22.29	15.28	458.37
11/8/17 18:30	3:01:09	7.03	45.35	47.61	10.90	89.10	183	119.49	56.58	139.00	21.00	21.00	99.78	100.22	2047	476	3.10	175	3.17	0.69	27.00	18.52	17.58	12.06	325.66
11/8/17 18:30	3:00:24	7.26	29.47	63.27	28.07	71.93	229	124.71	50.68	114.00	42.00	42.00	99.97	101.12	2062	456	2.68	122	2.80	0.50	23.00	11.41	25.35	12.57	289.21
11/8/17 18:30	3:00:11	17.98	25.34	56.67	17.76	82.24	209	130.06	56.05	116.00	25.00	25.00	99.93	100.40	2357	438	3.00	169	2.93	0.56	27.00	15.00	20.14	11.23	303.24
11/8/17 18:29	3:01:34	20.28	29.12	50.61	37.68	62.32	198	125.78	54.72	121.00	36.00	36.00	99.94	100.58	2154	417	2.84	127	3.29	0.43	31.00	15.06	20.33	8.78	272.20
11/8/17 18:31	3:00:04	40.46	40.33	19.21	40.84	59.16	158	140.75	71.75	146.00	32.00	32.00	99.81	100.40	2214	412	3.04	201	3.30	0.62	31.00	13.39	16.01	9.89	306.50
11/8/17 9:50	31:05	12.41	42.26	45.33	50.14	49.86	192	126.57	64.70	88.00			99.41	100.22	423	171	5.65	44	2.81	0.57	15.00	8.51	12.62	7.16	107.42
11/8/17 18:30	3:00:29	8.71	51.91	39.38	17.66	82.34	221	132.12	60.71	147.00	23.00	23.00	99.97	100.58	2057	578	3.68	94	2.47	0.54	30.00	13.56	24.78	13.44	335.95
11/8/17 18:31	2:59:49	2.88	45.36	51.76	29.74	70.26	188	120.13	36.89	124.00	26.00	26.00	100.09	100.76	2261	563	3.34	112	2.48	0.42	19.00	12.51	26.98	11.25	337.48
11/8/17 18:31	2:59:34			100.00	9.71	90.29	165			98.00			95.18	95.18	1899	454	2.89	116	2.42	0.56	21.00	16.01	26.99	15.00	285.00
11/8/17 18:32	2:59:24	19.98	38.55	41.47	40.68	59.32	204	132.94	43.92	133.00	39.00	39.00	100.11	100.94	2360	549	3.73	161	2.85	0.76	34.00	20.12	5.04	3.84	80.71
11/8/17 18:32	2:59:29	13.25	42.12	44.63	29.92	70.08	198	130.82	57.94	167.00	24.00	24.00	100.06	100.76	2266	545	3.72	149	2.79	0.59	22.00	19.14	17.36	10.27	349.29
11/8/17 18:46	2:59:46	9.57	36.95	53.49	45.53	54.47	236	146.73	49.22	74.00	27.00	27.00	100.61	101.48	2467	585	3.59	152	1.96	0.55	26.00	12.06	28.89	15.84	348.46
11/8/17 18:32	2:59:16	59.46	39.10	1.44	87.65	12.35	195	160.35	23.07	65.00	19.00	19.00	100.84	102.56	3044	1067	6.78	218	2.59	0.74		19.16	20.97	15.45	401.83
																		99	1.51	#DIV/0!			#DIV/0!	#DIV/0!	583.07
		18.63	39.65	44.79	36.32	65.59	199.67	132.83	53.35	120	30.00	30.00	99.76	100.50	2172.52	530.58	3.71	149.12	2.72	#DIV/0!	27.06	15.78	#DIV/0!	#DIV/0!	326.07
		13.96	8.50	19.61	18.29	19.63	16.65	10.05	11.13	27	9.01	9.01	1.15	1.41	511.38	179.74	1.03	46.26	0.44	#DIV/0!	5.37	3.77	#DIV/0!	#DIV/0!	111.03
		32.59	48.15	64.39	54.61	85.23	216.32	142.88	65.08	147	39.01	39.01	100.92	101.92	2683.89	710.72	4.74	195.38	3.16	#DIV/0!	32.43	19.54	#DIV/0!	#DIV/0!	437.10
		4.67	31.15	25.18	18.02	45.96	183.02	122.78	42.82	93	20.99	20.99	98.61	99.09	1661.14	351.23	2.68	102.85	2.28	#DIV/0!	21.68	12.01	#DIV/0!	#DIV/0!	215.04

Printed in the USA
CPSIA information can be obtained
at www.ICGtesting.com
LVHW081207161123
764032LV00006B/498